THE GUARDIAN CROSSWORD BOOK NO. 2

**Also by the same author
and available in Coronet Books:**

The Guardian Crossword Book No. 9

The Guardian Crossword Book No. 2

Edited by John Perkin

with a foreword by Ivor Brown

CORONET BOOKS
Hodder and Stoughton

Coronet edition 1968
Second impression 1972
Third impression 1980
Fourth impression 1980
Fifth impression 1986
Sixth impression 1986

Printed and bound in Great Britain for Hodder and Stoughton Paperbacks, a division of Hodder and Stoughton Ltd., Mill Road, Dunton Green, Sevenoaks, Kent (Editorial Office: 47 Bedford Square London, WC1 3DP) by Hazell Watson & Viney Limited, Member of the BPCC Group, Aylesbury, Bucks

ISBN 0 340 10903 3

FOREWORD

The publisher of a Book of Crosswords is true to the early history of a diversion whose popularity began when a collection was taken up. The chronicles have been related by Mr. MacNutt, known to his own as Ximenes, in his book on 'The Art of the Crossword'. Some may complain that artifice would suit the title better than art, but in the hands of the masters the weaving of the tangled web has produced a textile of such intricacy that to claim the status of an art seems to me well justified.

The game was long an elementary one suited to the grown-up children's hour. The Father Founder was Arthur Wynne of Liverpool, a journalist who emigrated to America and there began to compose his simple verbal patterns which he could sell to the 'Sunday World' of New York. That was in 1913. He did not set a fashion or create a craze until ten years later. Then the young publishing firm of Simon and Schuster put fifty of Wynne's problems into a book and sold half a million. Nowadays any rapid growth has to be called 'an explosion'. Crosswords exploded, but the bang did not at first send up a brilliance of ingenious mental fire-works. There was no catering then for the academic Double Firsts.

When the pastime was imported by the English Press there was a double development. The fairly easy puzzle was much liked by the arm-chair solver and the traveller who, having to fill his daily hour in the train, did not carry a dictionary from the home to the office. But the men of learning also found that here was a fascinating toy. The addiction became a Professor's Love-Story and a Don's Delight. What might be called the Higher Transverbalism flourished in the Senior Common Rooms where lurked the setters as well as solvers of a problem, fertile in the most complicated fabrications. Thus the Crossword had a genuinely national appeal. It was increasingly devised for children and the normal adult. It became a recondite pleasure of the sages and the specialists, an Intellectual's Joy.

So abtruse were some of the clues devised in the Academes and Barchesters that the B.B.C.'s 'Listener', which was created to do for the wiseacres what 'The Radio Times' was doing for the ordinary absorber of air-borne entertainment, printed Crosswords constructed by a learned Prebendary of Wells Cathedral whose non-de-plume was Afrit. At one time Afrit's compositions were so elusive that a prize was offered for any correct solution. That largesse had to be abandoned because the Clever Dicks (or Dons) managed to cope with the Prebendary's contrivance of bewilderment. The lucky dip had to replace the award for merit.

The torturing species of Crossword whose nature as well as name suggested mental crucifixion attracts to its own enraptured masochists. But the popular newspapers continued to offer simplicity for their millions while the more serious Press accepted the advice of Horace that you will go safest in the middle. Hence the wide adoption of the middle-brow puzzle. Its solution demanded a fairly wide acquaintance with the English language and sometimes with the common words of foreign tongues. It assumed sufficient familiarity with 'Eng Lit' to justify clues indicated in lines by well-known authors. It sometimes helped to have a lexicon and a Dictionary of Quotations handy. But they were not essential. The puzzle could get the average solver through two journeys home to office with his mind amusingly engaged. To that fashion of problem the 'Manchester Guardian'—I still think of myself as 'an M.G. man'—soon conformed. Its Crosswords I have regarded as what John Galsworthy's Forsytes provided to his public, Middle Classics.

I have been a steady practitioner with a taste for the testing not the tormenting puzzle. I cannot agree with Paul Jennings who wrote the charming Foreword for the first volume in this series. He was contemptuous of the addict's claim that the ploy has increased his wordpower and adds that his mind rejects the words learned in Crosswords. He did not want to be a dictionary-delver. But I am lexicon-prone. I have a quenchless appetite for words and an abiding curiosity as to their origins. Therefore I enjoy looking up a rarity and rummaging among its roots and neighbours. Mr. Jennings was indeed well answered in the anonymous introduction which followed his confession of likes and dislikes. Reference was made to the rich oddities to be discovered by looking up the words beginning with 'ga'. If you start to drink from a gallipot you will soon be gallivanting and galumphing galore in a gallopade (dance) if you have not first been bitten by a galliwasp (lizard).

Here is an example of my own. Having come across azalea in a Crossword as well as enjoying the sight of it in my garden I was eager to know why it was so named. So I consulted the Az's and was instructed that its Greek origin was based on its liking for dry, sandy ground. (That was odd since I live on clay soil in the London climate which constantly turns my patch into a bog without lethal and even with beneficent results for the Azalea.) Immediately after came the news that if I had an Azarole and an Azedarac I would possess a Neapolitan Medlar and a Bead-tree, the Pride of India. (Paul Jennings knows his India and should be fond of the latter). In the unlikely event of a really warm day I can sit azote (ungirt) among the flowers below under an azuline or azurine sky. Were I entertaining Jewish guests at Passover in similar weather I should feed them on azyme, unleavened bread, while we surveyed the azimuth of the heavens. If I sat alone I would be azygous, unyoked and free from the burden of conversation.

'What a load of old rubbish!' may be the retort. But my word-passion is not utilitarian. I do not admit the existence of 'useless knowledge'. One discovery in the dictionary leads to another. Serendipity, a lucky acquisition of a rarity, happens. (I met that word of Horace Walpole's in a puzzle.) My inquiry into azalean origins led me to some further cultural and ornithological lore. The word Aziola evoked an evening poem which begins

> 'Do you not hear the Aziola cry?
> Methinks she must be nigh'.

This query put to the poet caused him to think with dark foreboding that 'This Aziola was some tedious woman' looming up through the dusk. He was wrong. The answer came

> 'Disquiet yourself not;
> 'Tis nothing but a little downy owl'.

This led to some lyrical rejoicing in the sad cry of the fluffy bird who was not after all a feminine bore. The author of the poem was P. B. Shelley. Odd words lead to exalted as well as odd places.

Words that begin with 'a' and end with 'a' are very useful to the setters of crosswords. So are those with a final 'i'. One gets tired of elemi, a type of resin, and okapi, an 'African ruminant animal'. But what is to be done with the terminal vowels? The Italians are of assistance with their personal names, their operas, and their victuals. Clever setters manage somehow to cope with the difficult terminations, and I am constantly amazed at their ingenuity.

I have never entered into the creative side of the puzzle-game. It seems to me a labour beyond my reach for several reasons. How is one to judge whether the clue provided is too easy or too difficult? Take, for example, a word naturally in mind as I am writing, Guardian. If in my clue-construction I offered 'watchful Scot at the end of a train' would that be dismissed as deplorably obvious? Frequent resort is made to the anagram, 'a transposition of letters in a word to make a new one'. I wondered whether I could suggest anagram by an anagram? Three 'a's' in eight letters are defiant. There might be a plant or a place called Managra but I cannot find any escape that way. Anagram with 'G', 'r', and 'm' as well as three 'a's' brings grammarian to mind. One of the present tricks is to indicate a fairly short word by using a longer one and then indicating the letters to be omitted. In this case the surplus letters make rim. I might say of anagram 'A verbal twist, theme of a Robert Browning funeral with a broken edge left out. (8)'. I do not know how many of my solvers are Browningites and this could be dismissed as tortuous and tiresome in the extreme. I admire the tact with which setters assess the amount of difficulty agreeable to their public. I cannot rival them and do not seek to intrude on their gainful employment. In any case I do not know the amount of their gain which I hope is satisfactory to both employers and employed. Their rewards, which I suppose are subject to taxation, are well-earned income.

So I limit myself to investigating the tangled webs and hope not to be completely deceived by the deceptive clues. I unravel, if I can, what others spin and wish similar happy extrication to all who do the same. I cannot devote the whole of Sunday to exploring a verbal labyrinth. The Guardian puzzles, the middle-of-the-way compositions, do not hold me up too long and get me down in despair. Rose Macaulay once said that time-killing is a shocking thought. I agree. Time is not for slaughter but for enjoyment. Crosswords are time-fillers and in far more subjects than etymology they 'contribute to further education' or, if you cannot endure that kind of talk, they put you wise about your language. On then galumphing to the verbal gallopade in which you may encounter a gallimaufrey of galoots and gallow-glasses (assorted soldiery) capering in their galligaskins (loose breeches) amid the aromatic galingale, a melodious plant-name well used by Tennyson. The crossword leads to the dictionary. Any letter will do. Try the 'J's' offering joy all the way, from jabbernowl, a stupid lout, to the ill-omened jynx which is a bird in the trees. Presumably, unlike the aziola, it croaks. But enough of lexicography. Go to it. Unravel.

Ivor Brown

1

ACROSS

1. She spelled death by calm design (4, 7).
8. Heartless 16 (4).
10. Brown, following Milton's friend, is able to identify 1's victim (4, 6).
11. Noble part of Scotland known to 10 (4).
14. Superior vassal (5).
15. Some pop a question that cannot be seen through (6).
17. I denied female character? Yes over-weight (6).
19. Lofty Glencoe relatives, weird 12 (3, 5, 7).
20. Ball to spin but not in this place (6).
22. Little Reginald, mixed-up lad, had intense look (6).
23. Shrub as all discovered (5).
24. Vegetables may turn up at Scotland's capital (4).
27. 'Down in the forest something stirred'? (Fatally for 1's relict!) (6, 4).
28. 8's trick (4).
29. They secure the progress of animals from shore to shore around Spithead (5-6).

DOWN

2. Bird up, birds down (4).
3. American pull (4).
4. Roman magistrate rejected the Spanish idea (6).
5. They dominate pages—by standard wrinkles? (6, 9).
6. 22 down was one of them mentioned by 19. That's more than esoteric! (6).
7. The existing team told to go in to take charge (7, 4).
9. The way out ever ploughed earth needs courage (5, 5).
12. Hosea's story misrepresented 19 (11).
13. Verse features barred to the poetess? (4, 6).
16. From Peru she returns as teacher (5).
18. Art supporter's unconstrained manner, taking a pound (5).
21. Point to sporting gear doctor obtained for a northerner (6).
22. Welsh county is 1's husband's original title (6).
25. Lake entertainer (4).
26. There's nothing to the German river (4).

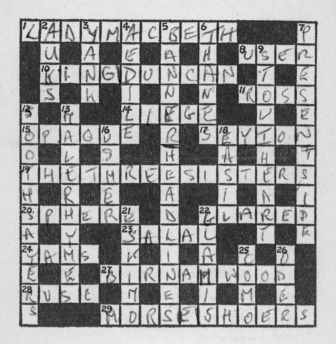

2

ACROSS

8. 10. (or 10 of 8) The girl is in the show—it's spectacular on the wings (8-4).
9. Innings completed with 100 per cent strike? (3, 3).
10. See 8.
11. See 24 down.
12. See 20.
14. 23's work has its place, but this is the latest idea for travel! (8).
15. Smears where one sleeps on a new bus (7).
17. Rule about the edge of a slope (7).
20. 12. Keep to nonstarters in Durham (8-2-4).
22. See 24 across.
23. Female boy, not his own, linked 20 and 11 (10).
24. 22 across. Rocket (see 14)? You need alternating current to cool it, (4, 6).
25, 26. Concern with clothes? (6, 8)

DOWN

1, 2. The solitary plaything of Gilbert Bennett (8, 4).
3. Religious aspiration on the river (6).
4. Wander a long way round to a city in Italy (7).
5. American 24 across: aim, Canal Turn (8).
6. Intrigue about a guest getting cut short quietly: there's always trouble here! (6-4).
7. Funny mood? (6).
13. Free man breaks the ice rising overhead (10).
16. 007's round the candle-flames, like 20 and 11 (4, 4).
18. Upper room mis-arranged in Athenian style (8).
19. One who knows the rise of a 22 across song (7).
21. Summer? It's nearly fall (6).
22. Britannia succeeded where he failed (6).
24. 11. Lady Windermere's fan (4, 10).

Solution to 1

ACROSS

1 Lady Macbeth; 8 User; 10 King Duncan; 11 Ross; 14 Liege;
15 Opaque; 17 Seyton; 19 The Three Sisters; 20 Sphere;
22 Glared; 23 Salal; 24 Yams; 27 Birnam Wood; 28 Ruse;
29 Horse Shoers.

DOWN

2 Auks; 3 Yank; 4 Aedile; 5 Banner Headlines; 6 Thanes;
7 Present side; 9 Stout Heart; 12 Soothsayers; 13 Male Rhymes;
16 Usher; 18 Easel; 21 Eskimo; 22 Glamis; 25 Como; 26
Oder.

3

ACROSS

7. Piece of impertinence, returning the chemical (5).
8. Line by poet about duck in car! (4-5).
9. Poet writes painful things (5).
10. You might grasp this, for a change! (4-5).
12. New paper allowance is in readiness (11).
16. Mark backs the right bills (4).
17. Pole reads Keats's work, perhaps (5).
18. Card game's just a battle! (4).
19. USSR can't get such weapons distributed (7-4).
22. Sedatives, for musicians, perhaps? (9).
24. Beat might be changed? (5).
25. Send a formation in support, as a soldier might do (5, 4).
26. Articles come by river (5).

DOWN

1. Sweet drink, with chill on (9).
2. The conveyance of ecstasy? (9).
3. Time to eat? (4).
4. Supplies reading for sister, perhaps (11).
5. Cash surplus for Romeo (5).
6. Northern cry of welcome? (5).
11. Perhaps a Norfolk angler employed by the BBC? (11).
13. Brook's tenant? (5).
14. Alf Lee got a new musical instrument (9).
15, 20. Speaker, full of pluck but in low spirits? (4, 2, 3, 5).
21. Suppose there's nothing on the tree? (5).
23. The others in the bar? (4).

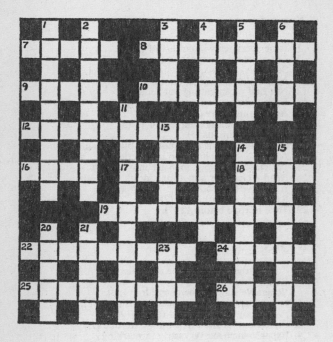

Solution to 2

ACROSS

8 Paradise; 9 All Out; 10 Bird; 11 Darlington; 12 On Tees;
14 Rocketry; 15 Bedaubs; 17 Slipway; 20 Stockton; 22
Citato; 23 Stephenson; 24 Loco; 25 Vested; 26 Interest.

DOWN

1. Patience; 2 Card; 3 Hindus; 4 Ferrara; 5 Maniacal; 6
Plague Spot; 7 Humour; 13. Emancipate; 16. Both Ends;
18 Atticism; 19 Gnostic; 21 Totter; 22 Canute; 24 Lord.

4

ACROSS

1. Issue specimen without list of 12 (7).
5. Tot returned in expensive foreign 12 (7).
10. See 24.
11. National colour of 12 (6, 4).
12. Not half mean cutting out food (6).
13. Each term's superlative produce (3, 5).
14. Active aim curler developed (9).
16. Road test almost complete in 12 (5).
17. Timely conditions (5).
19. Call and go to tie in a knot, i.e. bind together (9).
23. Armed but only in tattoo production (8).
24. 10. Novelist follows monster into 12 (10).
26. Read a clue if at a loss for a drink (4, 2, 4).
27. A relative for a boy (4).
28. Rude stable I fashioned (7).
29. Take in rope before 12 (7).

DOWN

2. Foot of the extinct roc he exhumed (7).
3. Relinquish a vacation (5).
4. Venerable stag in Aberdeenshire (3, 4).
6. Is it necessary for a number to rush . . . (6).
7. . . . cutting out from bird range? (9).
8. Flatter one of the French now overdue (7).
9. Expense incurred very early in marking handkerchiefs? (7, 6).
15. Animal without a limb makes 12 (9).
18. With some hauter university identifies a 24 (7).
20. The smoker's vessel? (7).
21. On a second floor—four altogether in braces (3-4).
22. 24 amused? Could be (6).
25. Somewhere a dyer is on hand (5).

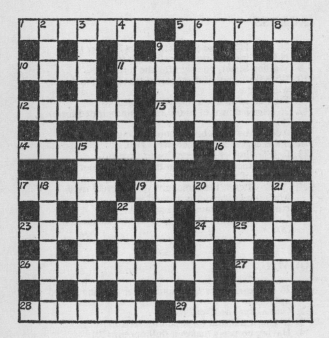

ACROSS

7 Nitre; 8 Dash-Board; 9 Burns; 10 Gear Lever; 12 Preparation; 16 Scar; 17 Anode; 18 Loos; 19 Scatter Guns; 22 Composers; 24 Pound; 25 Stand Easy; 26 Lethe.

DOWN

1 Liquorice; 2 Transport; 3 Date; 4 Thermometer; 5 Lover; 6 Greet; 11 Broadcaster; 13 Trout; 14 Flageolet; 15 Down In The; 20 Mouth; 21 Opine; 23 Rest

5

ACROSS

1. 26 after 11: I take you with me to 23 river (8).
5. N.B. 23 form (Cato is implicated) (6).
9. Watling Street, one sign for the birds (8).
10. With the decay of mechanised transport the donkey will follow (6).
11. First 26 of 23 20: a month we object to (8).
12. 26 after 1 down, of mural fame (unaspirated form) (6).
14. Address by a celebrity about casting a clout (10).
18. Ships engorged in quiet rivers (10).
22. Call the holder conservative to boot (6).
23, 20. See the leader chap in the 'Times' about the domain of the 26s (3, 5, 6).
24, 25. 26 after 8, the Stoic, giving us a cruel twist when the Epicurean is around (6, 8).
26. His destruction caused a scare (6).
27. Not wise enough to help give Chuter Ede lessons (8).

DOWN

1. 26 (44 years) after 6, a month after painting turned up (6).
2. Game over the river? (6).
3. It's most unusual for a painter to stop (6).
4. Having no peers makes a dull queen! (10).
6. 26 after 17—or I (8).
7. Great big crier, fit to bust (8).
8. 26 after 12, of mural fame: Dvorak, with four sharps? (8).
13. You are in the running for a legal place (5-5).
15. Long poem about half the rage (8).
16. A robin re-oriented in flight (8).
17. 26 after 1 across wreathed 11's head with lilac (8).
19. Old Glory—older than 23 20 (6).
20. See 23.
21. Returning South signifies unity—with 19 (6).

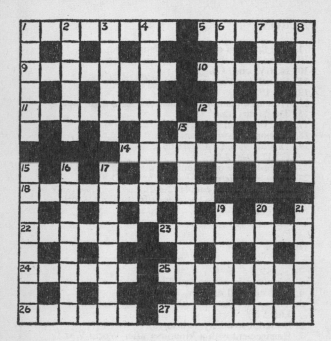

Solution to 4

ACROSS

1 Stilton; 5 Cheddar; 10 Zola; 11 Danish Blue; 12 Cheese;
13 The Cream; 14 Mercurial; 16 Mites; 17 Terms; 19 Colli-
gate; 23 Drumbeat; 24 Gorgon; 26 Cafe Au Lait; 27 Adam;
28 Bestial; 29 Gruyere.

DOWN

2 Trochee; 3 Leave; 4 Old Deer; 6 Hasten; 7 Debarring;
8 Adulate; 9 Initial Outlay; 15 Camembert; 18 Euryale; 20
Lighter; 21 Two Pair; 22 Medusa; 25 Ready.

6

ACROSS

1. The flower of an American family? (8, 5).
9. From which to vocalise or else instrumentalise (7).
10. Is R.V. one? (7).
11. French town entertains English relative (5).
12. See 19.
13. How passionate the Spanish get for a night out! (5).
15. The Stuart train? (5, 4).
17. One on the make makes a rare visit (9).
18. Having immortal longings? (5).
19, 12 and 19, 2. Last first and last second in the C.I.D. (9-9; 9-9).
22. In diplomacy one should be quiet (5).
23. They are different at last in the C.I.D. (3, 4).
24. A consequential couple (2-3-2).
25. The C.I.D. shares his interest to the limit, scoring nought (13).

DOWN

2. See 19.
3. It's sharp in buying or selling (5).
4. Conventional number, 1099 (5).
5. The Lord's disturbed about an abstainer being killed (9).
6. Scale for weather, we hear (5).
7. Engagement with a Mounseer after World War I (6, 7).
8. Success in prompting in the C.I.D. (13).
10. Artist bringing a lorry to a ditch (7).
14. Philtre for removal outside church (4-5).
15. Take back what's left, without science, home (7).
16. Boss in the C.I.D.—'e's in the same place (9).
20. Her it may be, also his (5).
21. No difficulty for a student to take pictures (5).
22. Guitarist's accent? (5).

7

ACROSS

1. Repeatedly doubled profits? (5, 3, 5).
9. Managed to load most of back of beam (7).
10. Get back in the middle of the train! (7).
11. Balance is seen in an American writer (5).
12. They might feel for camping experts, perhaps, when about fifty (9).
13. Fibre makes synthetic tiles (5).
15. Put vehicle back on list? That's easily managed! (9).
17. Flowers of the forest one put in the light? (9).
18. Appeal to some part singers (5).
19. Was expelled, as it proved? (6, 3).
22. Peasant was unruly at home (5).
23. Denies place, time, and direction of retreat (7).
24. Manage meeting before eleven? (7).
25. Sympathy for someone doing work of 12? (6-7).

DOWN

2. Make dog trail a fighter (9).
3. Children's publication? (5).
4. A rising doctor has something to concede (5).
5. Giant new T.A. gun holds up Indian city (9).
6. Perfect declaration of card-player? (5).
7. Two ways round the forest and one for crossing (8-5).
8. It is Mr Greene's composition for a poet and musician (13).
10. Is it not possible for sailors to be university men? (7).
14. The Spanish people go into late upset of the weather (9).
15. Sea-gods snort when coming up without object (7).
16. Soldiers alit on twisting in the club (9).
20. Rascal appears to regret holding up attempt (5).
21. Print quarter of Melville's work (5).
22. Class of explosive? (5).

Solution to 6

ACROSS

1 Virginia Stock; 9 Rostrum; 10 Version; 11 Niece; 12 Constable; 13 Hotel; 15 Royal Scot; 17 Arriviste; 18 Dying; 19 Detective; 22 Tacit; 23 The Yard; 24 So and So; 25 Criminologist.

DOWN

2 Inspector; 3 Gorse; 4 Nomic; 5 Throttled; 6 Climb; 7 French Mandate; 8 Investigation; 10 Vandyke; 14 Love Charm; 15 Rescind; 16 Coincides; 20 Their; 21 Easel; 22 Twang.

8

ACROSS

1. Faith that varies in its charity (12).
8. A theologian is no retrogressive essayist (7).
9. The peaceable girl returning in honour of the
   the group (7).
11. Fruit in the tundra is in short supply (7).
12. To colour deeply in anger is awkward (7).
13. A scoundrel turning over gold to half the guests (5).
14. Dance in or break the law (9).
16. 'I look through my tears on a —— clapping host.'
    (Thompson) (9).
19. Sent back drink at a hanging (5).
21. Mine gas presents problems (7).
23. A mischievous fellow joins others to get money
    advanced (7).
24. Start sedately swallowing food that's disdained (7).
25. A writer's French ring (7).
26. Beginners are erratic—he carries a flag (6-6).

DOWN

1. A little fish for two (7).
2. Sappers meeting with vindictiveness pause (7).
3. Rock and carelessly nod assent (9).
4. A fire in the garden burning leaves, etc. (5).
5. Figure on following on backing a horse (7).
6. Ground for a change of trainer (7).
7. They should know how to produce good crops (12).
10. It's often polite, so they say (12).
15. Epithet to flatter some faddist in Guernsey (9).
17. French article about turning fabulous bird in—or
    fabulous animal (7).
18. A denial makes me end it (7).
19. A man in the building trade goes around very
    quietly—he drinks a lot (7).
20. First, through embracing about a thousand and
    one (7).
22. A palanquin is partly closed and partly open (5).

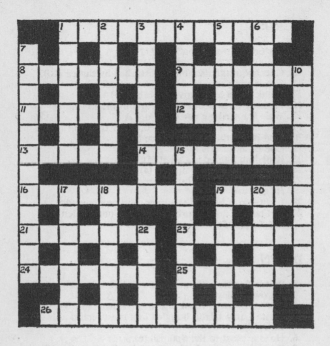

Solution to 7

ACROSS

1 Again and Again; 9 Transom; 10 Cortege; 11 Poise; 12 Tentacles; 13 Istle; 15 Tractable; 17 Gardenias; 18 Altos; 19 Turned out; 22 Swain; 23 Negates; 24 Preside; 25 Fellow Feeling.

DOWN

2 Gladiator; 3 Issue; 4 Admit; 5 Gargantua; 6 Ideal; 7 Stepping Stone; 8 Meistersinger; 10 Cantabs; 14 Elemental; 15 Tritons; 16 Battalion; 20 Rogue; 21 Typee; 22 Shell.

9

ACROSS

1. Hit one ill-treated buffoon? (11).
8. Has to alter part of porch (4).
10. Gets acquittal also, but is disturbed by charge (10).
11. Concerning case of scholar in Scotland (4).
14. Speak of an alternative tea-break (5).
15. Possibly hires about a thousand in France (6).
17. Weir is a striking person? (6).
19. Round sum a Mr Cole collected for the van? (8, 7).
20. Bird backs the Russian horse (6).
22. Cooler in quarrel? (6).
23. Kingdom altered sea edict (5).
24. Child wouldn't buy much? (4).
27. Agree to include Ming restoration in task allotted (10).
28. Lightship is back in the river, one supposes (4).
29. Yet has a most disturbing effect on untravelled people (4-2-5).

DOWN

2. State of some without a home? (4).
3. Throw in play? (4).
4. Homes of logs? I love the arrangement! (6).
5. A rite Larry Dixon bungled in a most remarkable way (15).
6. He is a beast to the Spanish (6).
7. Employees print the foreign strips (11).
9. Preacher who repeatedly makes a hit? (3-7).
12. Disposition of island stone—ten sorts (11).
13. Tries lemon squash in Herefordshire (10).
16. Animal in the river below Maidenhead (5).
18. Psychologist read novel about student (5).
21. Material could be tussore, not duck (6).
22. Man-trap for Jane Austen family? (6).
25. Comedian gets a pound rise (4).
26. Said enclosure is an eyesore (4).

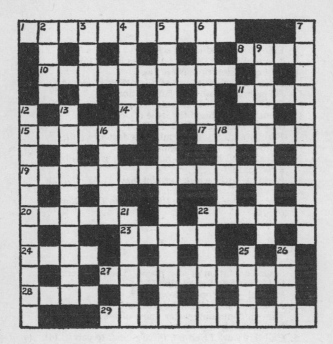

10

ACROSS

8. Emny's air-conditioned school for fathers (8).
9. The robber, enraged quietly goes ahead (6).
10. In a confusion of seaweed (6).
11. Others make better use of a few days in bed (4-4).
12. He embraces love with lamentation (4).
13. One way our birds migrate? (10).
15. Done it! I confused the issue (7).
16. Sink and cot for sale (2, 5).
18. Former audacity has resulted in dexterity (10).
19. Fellow turns point of knob (4).
20. What's been left out?—nothing; the girl will bring a charge (8).
22. Right, a Tory; wrong turning (6).
23. Be out of Town for the fair (6).
24. For a seaside speciality Herb goes to Gibraltar (4, 4).

DOWN

1. Stage adaptation of love poem, 'The Kiss'; enough to be worthy of emulation (3, 1, 4, 7).
2. Encore!—But tone it down (4, 7, 4).
3. Jet in dramatic climatic disturbance (5-5).
4. Though containing water, most of the house inside is remarkably dry (7).
5. Call this work? Sup up, there's nowt to cap it! (4).
6. Tending to delay but not against taking credit, as it arises, for lively notary (15).
7. In a state of decrepitude a car should be cheaper (2, 1, 7, 5).
14. Cartwheel well under four inches (10).
17. What some writers assume (3-4).
21. In practice, duty is not plain (4).

Solution to 9

ACROSS

1 Punchinello; 8 Stoa; 10 Absolution; 11 Oban; 14 Orate;
15 Rheims; 17 Lasher; 19 Armoured Columns; 20 Gander;
22 Breeze; 23 Ukase; 24 Mite; 27 Assignment; 28 Nore;
29 Stay-At-Homes.

DOWN

2 Utah; 3 Cast; 4 Igloos; 5 Extraordinarily; 6 Lionel;
7 Laundresses; 9 Tub-thumper; 12 Arrangement; 13 Leo-
minster; 16 Mouse; 18 Adler; 21 Russet; 22 Bennet; 25 Leno;
26 Stye.

11

ACROSS

9. 20's connection with the Stuarts (4, 5).
10. 20's connection with the Stuarts (5).
11. 12. 20's connection with the Stuarts (7, 3, 4).
13. Bowling gallery? (4).
14. Vapourings of set origin? (5, 5).
16. Nice day? Rotten! (2, 5).
17. Matthews has a row with a substitute ... (5-2).
19. ... which writer gets a following with an old thriller (5, 5).
22. Woman has a right, for this 10 is novel (4).
24. Suffers again on the river (7).
25. Sort of coil—tip to the wise (7).
26. Joker on the cart (5).
27. Order the way to go (9).

DOWN

1. Reformed characters at Workington who weren't born yesterday? (4, 1, 5, 2, 3).
2. Girl turning up on the wrong date screeched (8).
3. Make a profit as last year? (5).
4. Bob, it's my turn! Let me have a go at the correspondence! (8).
5. Among the expert, a meeting in Africa (6).
6. Worker precedes the élite cosmetically (4, 5).
7. One who writes poems about love, being transported? (6).
8. Gun dog in archery? Wrong sport! (9, 6).
15. Damaging effect of whisky and gin mixed (9).
17. Obviously not the wear for mountaineers (8).
18. Fit and for a bird (8).
20. Protestant or Parisian spirit (6).
21. Desire to live? (6).
23. 7 used at school (very obscure) (5).

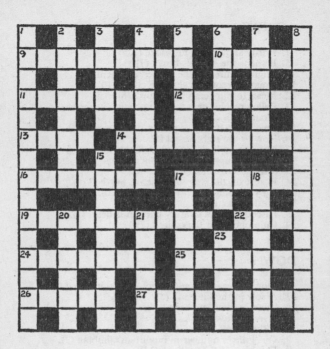

ACROSS

8 Seminary; 9 Pirate; 10 Tangle; 11 Rest Cure; 12 Moan; 13 Southwards; 15 Edition; 16 In Stock; 18 Expertness; 19 Node; 20 Omission; 22 Rotary; 23 Blonde; 24 Mint Rock.

DOWN

1 Set A Good Example 2 Sing Another Song; 3 Water-spout; 4 Hydrous; 5 Opus; 6 Procrastinatory; 7 At a Reduced Price; 14 Handspring; 17 Pen-name; 21 Iced.

12

ACROSS

1. Hardy shows skill in bridge (7).
5. Perhaps the driver's boss? (7).
10. Might be fired in the first engagement (4).
11. Young person has share in climb (10).
12. Mean to put scrap tin on tip? (6).
13. Fallen meteor causes dire upheaval in certain ground (8).
14. I wouldn't stand for such a punishment! (9).
16. Row to the right vessel (5).
17. The way to look for one in flight (5).
19. Claimant appears before offer is made (9).
23. Strong nets, round at back (8).
24. Resort on the way to Moscow, maybe? (6).
26. Ugly woman novelist on board? (10).
27. Futile style of speech? (4).
28. Discourse is awkwardly curt, in general (7).
29. Only one 'r' in Berkshire? (7).

DOWN

2. Flower, vegetable and about one fruit raised (7).
3. A row in the kitchen? (5).
4. 'Juan in Hell,' perhaps? (7).
6. Nymphs love studies (6).
7. Sally's trip? (9).
8. Girl joins a number in mountain climbing (7).
9. Thinking of the motive? (13).
15. Seen in the road drunk, without a complaint (4-5).
18. Needing a valve, walked into a driving place . . . (7).
20. . . . in which the right vehicle stands in a row (7).
21. A pound note, I changed, being in high spirits (7).
22. Composer finds silver in Wren building (6).
25. Dutch leader meets greedy king (5).

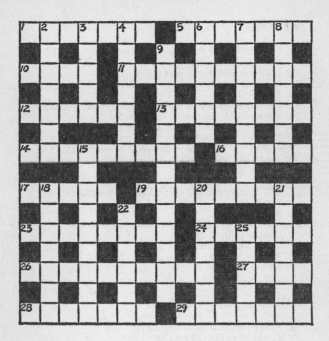

ACROSS

9 Nell Gwynn; 10 Amber; 11 William; & 12 And Mary;
13 Tate; 14 Steam Radio; 16 In Decay; 17 Stand-in; 19 Ghost
Train; 22 Ever; 24 Reaches; 25 Politic; 26 Wagon; 27
Direction.

DOWN

1 Know A Thing Or Two; 2 Ululated; 3 Again; 4 Symmetry;
5 Indaba; 6 Hand Cream; 7 Aboard; 8 Greyhound Racing;
15 Scotching; 17 Slippers; 18 Dovetail; 20 Orange; 21 Reside;
23 Black.

13

ACROSS

1. Loners? Tripe! When properly organised, they're too gregarious (11).
8. Irishman returns to post (4).
10. 'All that is human must —— if it does not advance' (Gibbon) (10).
11. Primate is back in a different mood, with gold (4).
14. Settler in Mercia could be right (5).
15. The Spanish swimmer is mischievous (6).
17. Beset also, 10 hides something on the roof (6).
19. Is Dan in? R.A. came in—upset tribesmen (8, 7).
20. Animosity shown when part of cardinal's insignia is back-to-front (6).
22. Receipts—counterfeit money to me (6).
23. 20? That's nothing; one is kept in, speechless almost (5).
24. She got up (4).
27. Slave-driver is to question teams involved in transfer (10).
28. Gorse's universal law (4).
29. They bring in 22, showing how the priest is attired (11).

DOWN

2. Fate of green ornithologist (4).
3. Consumes assorted teas (4).
4. Henry turned up carrying money—you can wash with it! (6).
5. Outlandish preserve has character (9, 6).
6. Heartless diggers demolished mountains (6).
7. Warning plan criminals don't like (5, 6).
9. Umpire Hill succeeds one baronet transformed by artist (10).
12. The rum image of sloth, very old (11).
13. The flavour behind a morsel (10).
16. A certain horse displays quiet wrath (5).
18. The French study when loaded! (5).
21. The same chief area of influence (6).
22. Influence of a collision (6).
25. Last year's spot? (4).
26. To eat out is a bit of a fiddle (4).

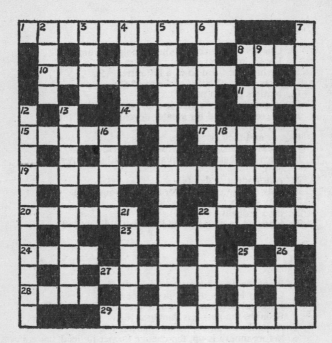

Solution to 12

ACROSS

1 Spartan; 5 Foreman; 10 Sten; 11 Adolescent; 12 Intend;
13 Siderite; 14 Bastinado; 16 Liner; 17 Stair; 19 Pretender;
23 Stalwart; 24 Redcar; 26 Gorgonzola; 27 Vain; 28 Lecture;
29 Reading.

DOWN

2 Petunia; 3 Range; 4 Abaddon; 6 Oreads; 7 Excursion;
8 Annette; 9 Consideration; 15 Tail Light; 18 Tetrode; 20
Terrace; 21 Elation; 22 Wagner; 25 David.

14

ACROSS

9. Our vet is disturbed about complaint from a French town (9).
10. Perhaps birds do so in a hill retreat (5).
11. Gets better of court exchanges? (7).
12. Notices broken part (7).
13. War tribute to French leader—retired (4).
14. A growing need for greater development of pupils ... (10).
16. ... and their protectors? (3-4).
17. Dispute makes NCO cross with nurse? (7).
19. Dress to change into going round a house, perhaps (10).
22. Actor sounds edgy (4).
24. Play a form of ecarte for about a pound (7).
25. City connected with fashion? (7).
26. Bird brought down? (5).
27. Hangers-on acquired by Brazilian builders? (9).

DOWN

1. Plant the herb Amos felt might do (4, 2, 9).
2. Clumsy lout on a river in France (8).
3. Effectual advantage of a sound curtain, perhaps (5).
4. Bedaubs the part less damaged (8).
5. Animal with streak round quarters (6).
6. Before month is up, ten change former judicial decision (9).
7. Has capacity to raise charge? That's the idea! (6).
8. Bear has a way with natives, in a manner of speaking (8, 7).
15. Acts to rid settlement of despots (9).
17. Flier secures the levers (4-4).
18. Animals in river, and lots of terriers (8).
20. 'Lesser —— without the Law' (Kipling) (6).
21. Vagrants in the dock? (6).
23. Chief could cause endless strife (5).

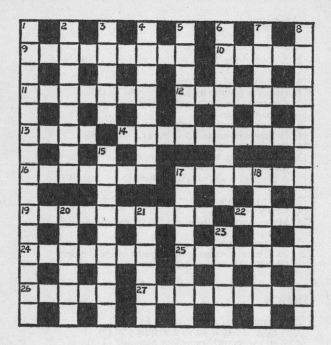

Solution to 13

ACROSS

1 Interlopers; 8 Mail; 10 Retrograde; 11 Ebor; 14 Angle;
15 Elfish; 17 Slates; 19 American Indians; 20 Hatred; 22
Income; 23 Odium; 24 Rose; 27 Taskmaster; 28 Ulex; 29
Investments.

DOWN

2 Norn; 3 Eats; 4 Loofah; 5 Peregrine Pickle; 6 Ridges; 7
Alarm System; 9 Arbitrator; 12 Megatherium; 13 Aftertaste;
16 Shire; 18 Laden; 21 Domain; 22 Impact; 25 Stye; 26 Fret.

15

ACROSS

1, 5. One of the 28 29, perhaps with one of the New 27s (3, 4, 2, 5).
10. Frequent sequel to Noah (4).
11. He cures squints by turning this to 27 (10).
12. A man of local authority, endless unless Mohammedan (6).
13. A man of local authority, a marshal (8).
14. Outlaw who earns his living as a writer (9).
16. Bob isn't, so to speak, in the canon (5).
17. Return of the bird—P.S., it's on the crest of the wave (5).
19. A prophet is showing one where to buy rubbish? (5-4).
23. Sneer turned into ridicule round 16 Peter 27 (8).
24. Cow's wool? (6).
26. Mine—very small—about ten thousand— in Fife (10).
27. Opening drink? (4).
28, 29. Church worms swallow some of the slander from 24, 23, 13, and 10 (7, 7).

DOWN

2. A man gets at a woman like Erica (7).
3. A man of battle wants a writing pad (5).
4. Wait expectantly or go out hunting? (4, 3).
6. Many tears are shed by d—— fools! (6).
7. At which things happen between notes (9).
8. Is perfect (3-4).
9. Source of fruit for barbers—wet and dry (10, 3).
15. A good sort of tempter taking in a foreign husband (9).
18. Wise little girl has something to eat, affecting modesty (7).
20. Clothing a spy wrapped round a block (7).
21. 'Go prick thy face and —— thy fear' (Macbeth) (7).
22. North Carolina follows its country with direction of employment (6).
25. Partitions in the fireplace (5).

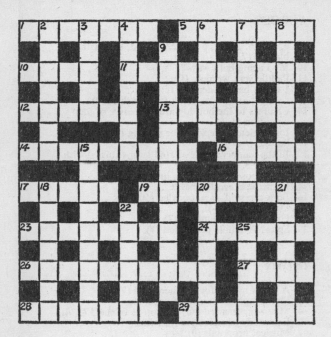

Solution to 14

ACROSS

9 Trouville; 10 Roost; 11 Rallies; 12 Section; 13 Feud;
14 Belladonna; 16 Eye-lids; 17 Contend; 19 Habitation;
22 Kean; 24 Electra; 25 Bristol; 26 Eider; 27 Parasites.

DOWN

1 Star of Bethlehem; 2 Toulouse; 3 Avail; 4 Plasters; 5
Weasel; 6 Precedent; 7 Notion; 8 Standard English; 15
Dictators; 17 Crow-bars; 18 Edentata; 20 Breeds; 21 Tramps;
23 First.

16

ACROSS

1, 5, 12, 16, 24, 27, 6 and 22. (Read, too, with a
   blank!) (7, 7).
10. Mr Facing-both ways? (4).
11. Paddle very wrongly (10).
12. 1 doing badly—deep 27 (6).
13. Catch it at quarter past? Ponder this! (8).
14. Changes to the hot dog are indicative of fine
    condition (4, 5).
16. Incompletely prepared for putting on (5).
17. See 8.
19. In the manner demonstrated swans turned with
    ease (2, 3, 4).
23. A composer has nothing in Russia (8).
24. Primrose is sensational (6).
26. Belts are sold, Ben, buckled (10).
27. Dismal athlete (4).
28. Group with its outlaws (7).
29. Spits? A simple perversion (7).

DOWN

2. A queer notion for the merchant (7).
3. She complains at once if upset (5).
4. Much-experienced lady? Another of the 5 (3, 4).
6. Extremely conservative fruit (6).
7. Musical proposals (9).
8. 17. Principle to engage principal, a good man
   determined to boss (4, 3, 5).
9. Ghosts surrounding a very large policeman are
   instrumental in showing up 1, 5 (13).
15. Quarter on the pool indeed gave up hope (9).
18. The dragonflies among the food on a table (7).
20. Lay out outrageous sums for a rock plant (7).
21. Eve embraced disorderly lout showing an original
    curve (7).
22. Flower girl (6).
25. Balance some flail I brandish (5).

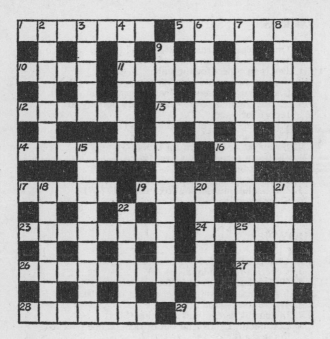

ACROSS

1 The Isle; 5 Of Wight; 10 Sark; 11 Orthoptist; 12 Sherif;
13 Alderney; 14 Proscribe; 16 Saint; 17 Spume; 19 Tripe-shop;
23 Guernsey; 24 Jersey; 26 Pittenweem; 27 Port; 28 Channel;
29 Islands.

DOWN

2 Heather; 3 Inker; 4 Look For; 6 Floods; 7 Intervals; 8 Has-
been; 9 Strawberry Bed; 15 Samaritan; 18 Prudish; 20 Pyjamas;
21 Overred; 22 Usance; 25 Repla.

17

ACROSS

1. Queen ceases to rule in Rhodesia? (8, 5).
10. It rings changes on the peel (9).
11. Penny to collect for the sailor . . . (5).
12. . . . sailor to employ insulting language . . . (5).
13. . . . cleaner to discourage vulgar gentleman . . . (9).
14. . . . serving man who swears there's nothing to report back about (7).
16. Carry out—I've collapsed in pain (7).
18. Dog harangue? That's fruity! (7).
20. Swaps tackle in return for tool (4-3).
21. Craft can encompass a river (9).
23. Pepper sounds cold (5).
24. Most ale comes to tankard from the wood (5).
25. Lime solution resulting from use of 13? (9).
26. Steps out of town? (7, 6).

DOWN

2. Change of mood; it's him or Lulu (3, 6).
3. Covering for headquarters (5).
4. Flute misses note—send for replacement (7).
5. Idiocy meant, strangely, ending up first class (7).
6. Where tree is fired? (9).
7. In general, as contract of letting (5).
8. Loft about, Lands End out of sight, canoe wrecked in the sea (8, 5).
9. Awe the fighter wrongly shows his opponent, perhaps (13).
15. Pitch red flier in pan for a grouse (9).
17. Formerly in charge on the river—explain . . . (9).
19. . . . hit back heartlessly at oarsman, one who bends the arm (7).
20. Frank about point to be crystallised (7).
22. Time's up for me to opt out (5).
23. Can the French be in what 13 does? (5).

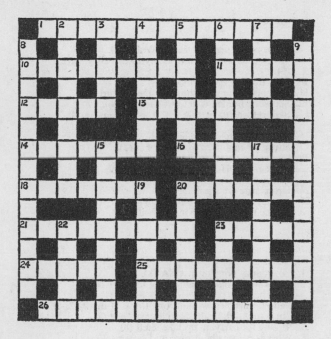

Solution to 16

ACROSS

1 Rainbow; 5 Colours; 10 Otto; 11 Depravedly; 12 Indigo; 13 Cogitate; 14 Good Heart; 16 Green; 17 Roost; 19 As Was Seen; 23 Borodino; 24 Yellow; 26 Bandoleers; 27 Blue; 28 Bandits; 29 Impales.

DOWN

2 Antonio; 3 Naomi; 4 Old Rose; 6 Orange; 7 Overtures; 8 Rule The; 9 Spectroscopes; 15 Desponded; 18 Odonata; 20 Alyssum; 21 Evolute; 22 Violet; 25 Libra.

18

8. Light on an unusual tree in Wales (8).
9. No sign of eruption in this mythical valley retreat (6).
10. Skin the fish gently first (4).
11. Odd nook the map shows in Devonshire (10).
12. Someone needed to let out garment (6).
14. Skill returns to batting with the odd gin—and practice! (8).
15. Applaud fashion familiar to Londoners (7).
17. Hires TV and does well out of it (7).
20. Chance of success in view? (8).
22. Walk round Holyhead looking for fibre (6).
23. Perceive rise in value? (10).
24. Drops rule for speaking (4).
25. Space travellers arrive by the back way (6).
26. Notice members carrying in poison (8).

DOWN

1. Low dance popular in USA (8).
2. Some stop a lightweight going into the ring, perhaps (4).
3. Familiar articles, without one thing of merit (2, 4).
4. Little tune—difficult air to a small girl (7).
5. Money for carrying up lake shell (8).
6. Worker comes about one, and boxer (10).
7. Firms have no standing in this case (6).
13. Records attempts to put down hangings (10).
16. Work can set puzzle in this sort of mine (4-4).
18. Excuses husband raising charges (8).
19. Ways to include the Water Music? (7).
21. Sets one right about training in school (6).
22. Wrinkle of use to soldiers? (6).
24. Put something in about the ceremony (4).

Solution to 17

ACROSS

1 Victoria Falls; 10 Telephone; 11 Drake; 12 Abuse; 13 Detergent; 14 Trooper; 16 Achieve; 18 Currant; 20 Cats-paw; 21 Catamaran; 23 Chili; 24 Almug; 25 Whitewash; 26 Country Dances.

DOWN

2 Ill Humour; 3 Topee; 4 Reorder; 5 Amentia; 6 Aldershot; 7 Lease; 8 Atlantic Ocean; 9 Featherweight; 15 Ptarmigan; 17 Explicate; 19 Thrower; 20 Candied; 22 Tempo; 23 Clean.

19

ACROSS

1. Natural growth by association, the right one (8, 6).
8. Natural growth? Heavens! He's vanished! (5).
9. Natural growth of a horse (8).
11. Dill due to be tricked (7).
12. Natural growth of Scotland's pride (7).
13. Natural growth in 9 (5).
15. Natural growth by a queen in musical comedy (4, 5).
17. Natural growth, me lad? Rubbish! (9).
20. 11-500 (5).
21. Gaping at extraction of colour in gentian . . . (7).
23. . . . all gain from exchange in Ceylon (7).
25. Natural growth in play (8).
26. Natural explanatory addendum to my statement—in Odessa I divulge (4, 1).
27. Natural growth by a Western hero? True possibly—it might suit you! (7-7).

DOWN

1. Acting as children in detachment may be (7, 1, 4).
2. Perfect a distribution (5).
3. Deny cries coming from official abode (9).
4. Decrees confused nonconformist (7).
5. Shakespearean character tossed up a Spanish coin to meet setback (7).
6. Mountains—altitude excellent (7).
7. Wordless duet tuner transposed (9).
10. Always upset about groups rejecting it with an improving effect (12).
14. A footnote, perhaps, requesting personal information (9).
16. Impossibly neuter in England? (9).
18. Issue of coot and emu (7).
19. Animal, vegetable, or mineral, naturally (7).
22. Prophet and Old Testament poet (5).
24. The last word from 'The Iliad' I eulogised (5).

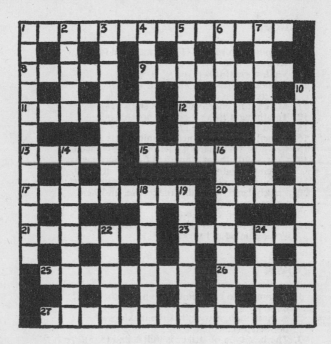

Solution to 18

ACROSS

8 Lampeter; 9 Avalon; 10 Peel; 11 Okehampton; 12 Mantle;
14 Training; 15 Clapton; 17 Thrives; 20 Prospect; 22 Thread;
23 Appreciate; 24 Rain; 25 Comets; 26 Nicotine.

DOWN

1 Baseball; 2 Opal; 3 At Home; 4 Arietta; 5 Calabash;
6 Carpentier; 7 Cocoon; 13 Tapestries; 16 Open-cast; 18
Evasions; 19 Strains; 21 Repton; 22 Trench; 24 Rite.

20

ACROSS

8. In mountain retreat Harold was used to servitude (8).
9. Well, cheers! (6).
10. American Missionary?—That was Charles Lamb, girl! (6).
11. Mixed it in once; went up in smoke (8).
12. The thought of a sleigh-ride appeals (4).
13. Food for the bearded? (6-4).
15. Stencil as per customers' requirements (7).
16. Consider how many get let out by reference (7).
18. Cost Smith about a hundred for replacements, which naturally has a dampening effect (6, 4).
19. Right in the city: superior unbleached linen (4).
20. Prickly head married without love, and went underground (8).
22. A summary? Carry on (6).
23. Country home on view, with set tea (6).
24. Wrong tie bound very high (8).

DOWN

1. Compromise between the soup and the fruit? (3, 6, 6).
2. A plain man, a trier; has the makings of a politician (15).
3. The best type of striker is well suited (5, 5).
4. This is a toadstool!—and he is the person one thanks (7).
5. Style in which 'Ichabod' has written (4).
6. Sea shanty? (8, 7).
7. And on one occasion about the beginning of the week, in a filthy place, all contrived to be punctilious about forms! (5, 2, 8).
14. Open on time; admit being upset (10).
17. It's made to show the wrong day (7).
21. Little soft cry (4).

Solution to 19

ACROSS

1 Primrose League; 8 Avens; 9 Chestnut; 11 Illuded; 12 Thistle; 13 Grain; 15 Rose Marie; 17 Poppycock; 20 Dodge; 21 Ringent; 23 Nilgala; 25 Marigold; 26 Saidi; 27 Heather Mixture.

DOWN

1 Playing A Part; 2 Ideal; 3 Residency; 4 Seceder; 5 Laertes; 6 Altai; 7 Unuttered; 10 Regenerative; 14 Appendage; 16 Middlesex; 18 Outcome; 19 Kingdom; 22 Eliot; 24 Adieu.

21

ACROSS

1. Give entertainment without wine? Disgusting! (8).
5. Possibly fears meeting hothead again (6).
9. and 10. Living on board? (5-3-6).
11. Essential for an effective speaker (8).
12. Like a bird at the back (6).
14. Might get some but is a temperate type (10).
18. Improve ale I'm brewing, so to speak (10).
22. Is it posted in a ship? (6).
23. Makes up tours round Orme's Head, as hostess does, perhaps (5, 3).
24. Players make singles (6).
25. Artist is a national prophet, perhaps (8).
26. Rubbish found beside the dam? (6).
27. Plant manufactures toys, so I'm going into it (8).

DOWN

1. Upsetting vehicle, gets let off—that's cunning! (6).
2. Nothing needs changing in Denmark! (6).
3. Organ makes a terrible din—the clue's about that (6).
4. Men Mrs Bone collected are not society people, perhaps (3-7).
6. A number take part in this game (8).
7. Rent collector gets fish up from warehouse (8).
8. Large number come in to tackle difficulty (8).
13. Still speaking of paper, perhaps (10).
15. Member appears to be interrupting visit from poet (8).
16. The cases could be the sailor's property, perhaps (3-5).
17. A large number rise awkwardly before the psalm (8).
19. Some extra desirable occupations (6).
20. Second in importance? (6).
21. Baby birds? (6).

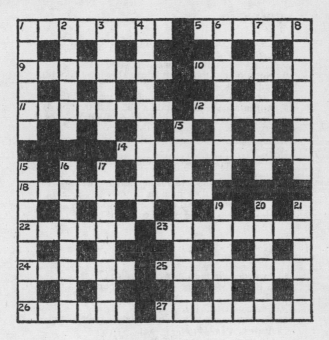

ACROSS

4. Careful about dress after too much conflict (3-5).
8. E.g. Silver cross on the piano (6).
9. Lump we shall raise our voices about (8).
10. Not a pound to enter a biter in the local gaol (8).
11. Indian silk—not alien corn? (6).
12. Corn 'alii' translated with hidden meaning (8).
13. Appearance remaining on a one-way street (4, 4).
16. Letter—the last one—that's in Guy Fawkes' day (8).
19. Statesman's backing of work during morning tea (4, 4).
21. Make a parson (perhaps) a fool, commonly: he ... (6).
23. ... (parson, the fool!) is in church—yawning? (8).
24. Transatlantic deck number for every week (5-3).
25. Complaint by a girl about a boy (6).
26. Hotelier has to dig out in college (8).

DOWN

1. Extended circle to prove prejudice (7).
2. A bonnet is strange wear for an Inquisition victim (9).
3. Brave couplet? (6).
4. Triumph song—West Indian bowler's bowling—draw near! (2, 5, 8).
5. Granny's relative rocks at speed (4-4).
6. Welshman of a seemly nature (5).
7. It suggests disengagement—from phone or finger (4, 3).
14. A huge ball could be ridiculous (9).
15. A rich man, Edward, without 21s (8).
17. I shall leave in enmity (3-4).
18. On half of the field (3, 4).
20. Edges around male jackdaw's home (6).
22. Express disapproval or teach (5).

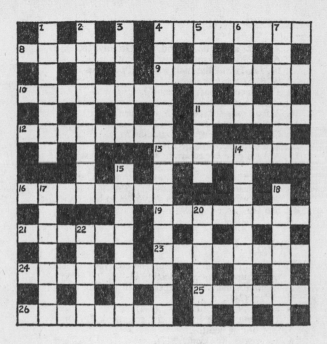

ACROSS

1 Shocking; 5 Afresh; 9 Bread and; 10 Butter; 11 Listener; 12 Astern; 14 Abstemious; 18 Ameliorate; 22 Packet; 23 Pours Out; 24 Eleven; 25 Landseer; 26 Litter; 27 Myosotis.

DOWN

1 Subtle; 2 Odense; 3 Kidney; 4 Non-members; 6 Foursome; 7. Entrepot; 8 Hardness; 13 Stationary; 15 Campbell; 15 Sea-chest; 17 Miserere; 19 Trades; 20 Moment; 21 Storks.

23

ACROSS

1. After 27's peculiar sound, I'm Granny! (6, 7).
8. After 27 and 1 across, the sole condition . . . (10).
9, 11, 12. . . . of the man who will 16 in his 17 (4, 8, 6).
14. The place of martyrology (5).
15. Put one in letters (5).
16. A frog may succeed in his career (2, 3).
17. Lots of people from the Marx Brothers' day (5).
20. Chart for the French Canadian? (5).
22. The purpose of camp? (6).
23. Am I a case for relations wanting the best food? (8).
25. 'Teach the young —— how to shoot' (Thomson) (4).
26. Secret weapon: Bob has a quarrel to his credit (5-5).
27. See 18.

DOWN

1. It takes personality to stop the coal industry being the arbiter of its own destiny (4-11).
2. Legal abstinence is a burden splitting half the nerves (3-4).
3. Hello! No rain or snow? (3-4).
4. The king of the Eternal city sounds dull! (10).
5. Got out of bed (4).
6. The reason for coffee? (7).
7. A 20, most likely, could make Kate accept Tiger (9, 6).
10. 9 if not high (4).
13. Deficiency in the British Museum—the song 'Going to Prison' (5, 5).
18, 27. Burns's mixed up with Scott re the weekend (7, 8, 5).
19. Authoress with bag and paper (4).
20. Is a fool about Burns's Mary (7).
21. A dog without a bone has to be self-assertive (7).
24. Sheep with ram's head in jug (4).

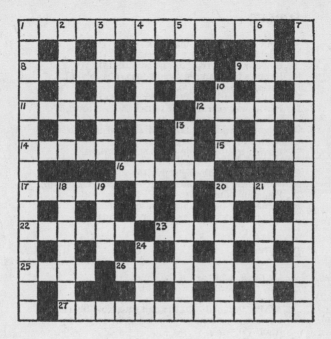

Solution to 22

ACROSS

4 War-weary; 8 Pirate; 9 Swelling; 10 Tolbooth; 11 Kincob;
12 Ironical; 13 Look Left; 16 Zinoviev; 19 Earl Grey; 21
Clothe; 23 Crevasse; 24 Fifty-two; 25 Malady; 26 Claridge.

DOWN

1 Bigotry; 2 Sanbenito; 3 Heroic; 4 We Shall Overcome;
5 Reef Knot; 6 Emlyn; 7 Ring Off; 14 Laughable; 15 Divested;
17 Ill-will; 18 Leg Side; 20 Rheims; 22 Tutor.

24

ACROSS

1. Time a P.C. mixed the drink? (8).
5. Capital proverb for a conflict? (6).
9. Emperor gives river to one country (8).
10. Reptiles from an old city in Asia, possibly (6).
12. Girl makes notes? (5).
13. Settles a girl into a fitting occupation (9).
14. By the way one is going round an Irish town, it's in an Irish castle (7, 5).
18. Might describe the Prime Minister as a skilled worker? (7-5).
21. Having trouble getting through the course? (2, 3, 4).
23. Association Jack might join (5).
24. Wood gets round old lawyer—needed backing (6).
25. Being animated? (8).
26. Female hat-maker, in this case (6).
27. Fire understood to be back in the range (8).

DOWN

1. He raises it in part of the church (6).
2. Ape the historian's work? (6).
3. Saint breaks train trip to see sailor (9).
4. Mixing the load with the unit rate, possibly (12).
6. Concerning a scholar of standing in an Italian resort (5).
7. Unusual stir over an attendant (8).
8. Clever fellow, but quarrelsome? (8).
11. Politicians are out by April? Later (7, 5).
15. Letters in a flood about a bad clue, I bet! (9).
16. Hero takes high place among experts (8).
17. It hinders production of the best coal (8).
19. Any amount of fruit over the river (6).
20. Concludes various friends are penniless (6).
22. Steven Todd's content with result (5).

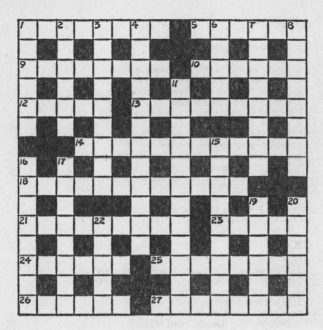

ACROSS

1 Sunday Morning; 8 Loneliness; 9 Long; 11 Distance; 12 Runner; 14 Tyrol; 15 Posit; 16 Go Far; 17 Races; 20 Maple; 22 Intent; 23 Ambrosia; 25 Idea; 26 Sword-stick; 27 Saturday Night.

DOWN

1 Self-determining; 2 Non-user; 3 All Hail; 4 Monochrome; 5 Rose; 6 Grounds; 7 Cigarette Packet; 10 Jump; 13 Black Maria; 18 Cotters; 19 Sand; 20 Morison; 21 Pushing; 24 Ewer.

25

ACROSS

1. Mild batting attack (11).
8. Bitter-sweet? (4).
10. Drink makes brutal detectives turn about (5, 5).
11. Some quiet-natured hot-head (4).
14. Sick at heart of the French part of France (5).
15. Compel to accommodate (6).
17. Newspaper term for the hoi-polloi (3-3).
19. Player, not keen on being the 9 of 1, 21 (5, 10).
20. One to milk, menace, and bully in the main? (3, 3).
22. Girl confusing aliens (6).
23. Latin joiner holds back Latin light and glory (5).
24. Cut round Canute's insurgent (4).
27. It appears to have no one father getting about equal to it (10).
28. Stem from a rare edition (4).
29. Rice grown in Rent-a-tree organisation (11).

DOWN

2. Conqueror without an accepted standard (4).
3. Loud where French and Latin collide (4).
4. Blow prince into the river (6).
5. King Asa's useless food content (8, 7).
6. Witness sends six to jug (6).
7. Now for the Roman road (11).
9. Atheist troubled with sin? Quite the contrary (10).
12. Valetudinarians have them; so far bromides hold the answer (6, 5).
13. Let Alfred the Poet sound the report (1, 4, 5).
16. Contact part of the target tonight (3, 2).
18. Beguile one of nine (5).
21. Take a pew. No, it might give offence (6).
22. Just a moment—in a way it has no point (6).
25. Puccini's dual carriageway? (4).
26. Formerly subject to the Establishment (4).

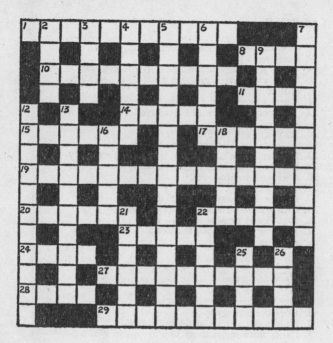

Solution to 24

ACROSS

1 Nightcap; 5 Warsaw; 9 Tiberius; 10 Sauria; 12 Viola; 13 Tailoring; 14 Blarney Stone; 18 Cabinet-maker; 21 In The Soup; 23 Union; 24 Lacked; 25 Creature; 26 Sheath; 27 Pyrenees.

DOWN

1 Native; 2 Gibbon; 3 Tarpaulin; 4 Adulteration; 6 Abano; 7 Servitor; 8 Wrangler; 11 Liberal Party; 15 Speculate; 16 Achilles; 17 Obstacle; 19 Figure; 20 Infers; 22 Event.

26

ACROSS

1. The wandering scholars seem repeatedly to execrate 24 (5, 5).
8. Don't go to them—and 22's at the fireside (4).
10. There's nothing in crossing the line: it doesn't last! (10).
11. Nursing proverbially 16 one of the 23s (4).
13. Too much French and Latin here to be nutritional (7).
15. '2! They —— the 8 and . . . (6).
16. . . . —— the 23' (Browning) (6).
17. Nothing doing? State what is serviceable (2, 4, 9).
18. It's the French way to get 'flu badly—sorry! (6).
20. Stick in the garden (6).
21. The 23 of 3 (7).
22. O for a 3! It may have a 20 down (4).
25. I leave Oslo on a second pilgrimage (10).
26. Mat like 11 or Johnsonian 8 (4).
27. My song is about evil treatment of violin strings, etc. (10).

DOWN

2. Star turn for those who 4 (4).
3. I fled the country (4).
4. It's worth having 2 in the last war (6).
5. Burns' adversaries show how to mount a campaign with a bent hatpin (15).
6. Norwegian informer includes this number (6).
7. Bad case: pretty girl takes in copper in high position (10).
9. Lesson laid out everywhere (2, 3, 5).
12. The psychologist's a funny fellow, old cock! (6-4).
13. Build fast, be sick, and resign (5, 2).
14. Countryman, as it were, sounds like urban religion (7).
15. Religious fliers eat honey in Australia (5-5).
19. In Paris the dear man is after the women (6).
20. Actors performing—with needles? (4, 2).
23. Wrong acts in which a 13 across is disastrous (4).
24. 23 and 8 from 3 (4).

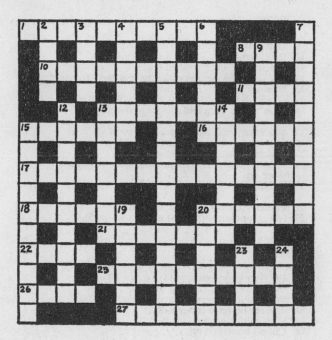

Solution to 25

ACROSS

1 Inoffensive; 8 Tart; 10 Rough Cider; 11 Etna; 14 Lille; 15 Oblige; 17 Rag-tag; 19 Blunt Instrument; 20 Dun Cow; 22 Selina; 23 Exult; 24 Edit; 27 Apparition; 28 Reed; 29 Entertainer.

DOWN

2 Norm; 3 Foul; 4 Exhale; 5 Skinless Sausage; 6 Viewer; 7 Straightway; 9 Antithesis; 12 Morbid Fears; 13 A Loud Noise; 16 Get to; 18 Amuse; 21 Weapon; 22 Strict; 25 Mimi; 26 Once.

27

ACROSS

9. Learns discipline and drive (9).
10. Quiet remark made in a seaside hotel (5).
11. No board is distinguished (7).
12. Old queen owing everything to one earl (7).
13. Western worker's inadequacy (4).
14. Having been bad, ask for savoury food (5, 5).
16. Most of the team had a meal to overcome depression (7).
17. Moorhen's peculiar internal secretion (7).
19. In church following inexperienced loud singer (10).
22. A drop of ink (4).
24. Vehicle that's less accommodating in the same place (7).
25. In Israel an attendant has to return before four (3, 4).
26. Parker's manner of speaking? (5).
27. Many a politician's agent gets a seat (4, 5).

DOWN

1. Receiver's confession? (15).
2. Putting out nine cats, for example (8).
3. Wounds in the most absent-minded way (5).
4. The tax on spice is steep (8).
5. Stick in this position (6).
6. Cheese came first (9).
7. Capital that is held by backward girl, five (6).
8. Looking back may give rise to levity or respect (15).
15. They like to see people in a stew! (9).
17. Tearing coat lining, male doctor makes great sacrifice (8).
18. Charm about fifty-four on being forgotten (8).
20. He's in Lucerne, staying with friends (6).
21. A six-footer may be nicest (6).
23. Shut up the establishment about sun-up (5).

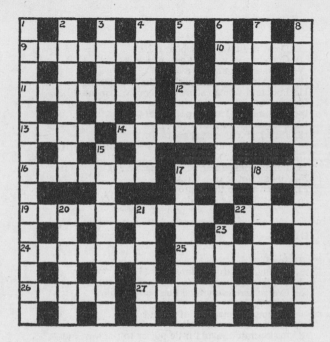

Solution to 26

ACROSS

1 Brain Drain; 8 Dogs; 10 Transitory; 11 Care; 13 Trophic; 15 Fought; 16 Killed; 17 In Good Condition; 18 Rueful; 20 Celery; 21 Persian; 22 Iron; 25 Christiana; 26 Dull; 27 Resinising.

DOWN

2 Rats; 3 Iran; 4 Desert; 5 Antiphlogistics; 6 Narvik; 7 Ascendancy; 9 On All Sides; 12 Jungle-fowl; 13 Throw Up; 14 Citizen; 15 Friar-birds; 19 Lecher; 20 Cast on; 23 Cats; 24 Rain.

28

ACROSS

1. Draw southwards by boat (6).
5. Corollary of a gimlet cut, which is ... (2, 1, 5).
9. ... indispensable to 6 6 (8).
10. Luggage taken in as well in the Caribbean (6).
11. Fool and woman share a solemn statement (12).
13. See 22.
14. Press the bell and run away? (4-4).
17. Everybody, to Butler (3, 5).
18, 19. 13 of Wilson's show (4-6).
20. Latin book and mount, perhaps, aesthetic, with few seats (7, 5).
23. Italian conspirator or a wrong 'un (6).
24. Giving notice of 6 6 (8).
25. 6 6 gives you the figure (8).
26. What does the dam do to the river? (6).

DOWN

2. See 3.
3, 2. English garden's farewell? (3, 4, 2, 4).
4. Trouble has surrounded the painters (6).
5. Everywhere everything done on the spot? (3, 4, 3, 5).
6. Making an anagram of 18 and 22 (8).
7. The use of clothing (5).
8. Back-scratchers add little power to the waves (3-7).
12. Umpire in the beauty contest won by Snow White (4, 6).
15. The plant on my right has been eaten by a goblin (3, 6).
16. In regard to 6 6, it would be telling! (8).
19. See 18.
21. 18 after a morning across the Atlantic (5).
22. 13. Volcano erupts: fruit set too soon? (8).

29

ACROSS

1. Trifles said carelessly, as politeness dictates (6, 5).
8. Force of return gets love game (4).
10. Tossed yacht a rope in 'Romeo and Juliet' (10).
11. Leaves producer of 'The Cherry Orchard' (4).
14. The right god for a sculptor? (5).
15. Plate being returned? (6).
17. More eager, like energetic type (6).
19. Finishes preparation for bombardment?
    (4, 3, 3, 3, 2).
20. Manages to make joins about one (6).
22. Trifling affront? (6).
23. Fly from a girl? (5).
24. Weather rule is sound (4).
27. Beats off-shore, and west to shipwreck (10).
28. Some of our general press (4).
29. Odd notches found in vegetables—they're in fruit,
    too (5, 6).

DOWN

2. He fell from a mare, perhaps (4).
3. Pressing need of course? (4).
4. Has upset associate in Africa (6).
5. Strains sustained during play (10, 5).
6. Recoil from a take-off of Krishna, possibly (6).
7. River girl managed to spill tea and fruit (11).
9. Tapes organ pieces in theatre, perhaps (5, 5).
12. Everyone might get 'flu, possibly though
    appearing omnipotent (3, 8).
13. Superficial knowledge, a quarter being of
    importance (10).
16. Celebrated in the bar (5).
18. Girl writes article in Spanish type (5).
21. Zoe's no sort to sleep (6).
22. Dramatist's original work for musical instruments
    (6).
25. Beach has cover overhead (4).
26. Man could be? I'll say! (4).

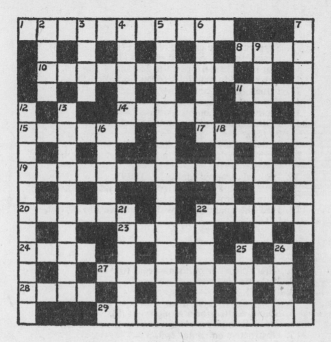

30

ACROSS

1. Support for the change of a 24 (7).
5. Obscurity for the friend of a 24 (7).
9. Not how Disraeli spelt the 24 (5).
10. The sound of the flute, for example? (4-5).
11. It may have a centre between the poles (10).
12. Was first and foremost a swan (4).
14. Victory Alan obtained with a 24 (11).
18. A little music—first number on the fiddle—for a 24 (11).
21. Order to stop in the ship (4).
22. Carbon, hydrogen and sulphur to a philosopher make a 24 (10).
25. Dick who turned on his heels? (9).
26. Love and a kiss at the front of the lake (2-3).
27. Wrings, formerly wrongs? (7).
28. Bird like Shakespeare with his native 10 (7).

DOWN

1. After other things it's an order (6).
2. Paths or pieces (6).
3. 10 (4, 1, 5).
4. How to move a caravan, that is to say (2, 3).
5. Sound written for a monograph (9).
6. 24. Guinea pieces always display the artist (8).
7. Obstructive en route (2, 3, 3).
8. Discretion in a heroine passed in the 17th century (4, 4).
13. Hero's variants will work with luck (5-5).
15. Old bird, lion's leader, within range (9).
16. Most of one meal, like most of the next, is impure (8).
17. David finds Bob in 5 across (8).
19. Sign of an audible clanger (6).
20. Top for aristocracy, bottom for marriage (6).
23. The endless trouble caused by the cast (5).
24. See 6.

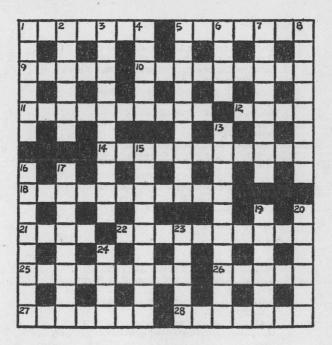

Solution to 29

ACROSS

1 Ladies First; 8 Faro; 10 Apothecary; 11 Tree; 14 Rodin; 15 Lamina; 17 Keener; 19 Puts The Tin Hat On; 20 Wields; 22 Slight; 23 Nymph; 24 Rain; 27 Horsewhips; 28 Urge; 29 Peach Stones.

DOWN

2 Adam; 3 Iron; 4 Sahara; 5 Incidental Music; 6 Shrink; 7 Pomegranate; 9 Apron Stage; 12 All Powerful; 13 Smattering; 16 Noted; 18 Ethel; 21 Snooze; 22 Shawms; 25 Lido; 26 Isle.

31

ACROSS

1. Character to make Goliath respond (3, 8, 3).
8. On charge it may bring tears to the eye (5).
9. Skin trouble comes from washing less often . . . (8).
11. . . . on the face of it (7).
12. Hold forth against decimal conversion (7).
13. Maxim of retrograde Bolshevik rogue (5).
15. See half that in Cheshire town (9).
17. Too weak, we hear, this time—gets torn badly in combat (9).
20. Composer enters last letter in catalogue (5).
21. Religion's first with priest-worker, one can be sure of that . . . (7).
23. . . . invest in worker, if abroad for example (7).
25. Write one and ten first time—sorry! (8).
26. A real ground to take in live stock (5).
27. Can be seen beneath, and in stable (14).

DOWN

1. Way to cook hot, coarse food? (12).
2. Canute, beginning to be covered by turning tide, gives order (5).
3. Interpretation of inordinate confusion when article is dropped (9).
4. Turned to cinders, we perceive (7).
5. He makes smooth show of amusement at rising colour (7).
6. Good reasoning makes pupil go up one, to top class (5).
7. On reflection, perhaps, about time they are done on stage . . . (9).
10. . . . current hit on here—round at the Coliseum perhaps (12).
14. Sly, shady character, according to Brooke? (5, 4).
16. Entire street hand out hats etc. from it . . . (4, 5).
18. . . . the rags from which dress is adorned . . . (7).
19. . . . piece in a hat got up by old seamstress . . . (7).
22. . . . headwear for a civil engineer? (5).
24. Son of Jesse Bailey rejected from the start (5).

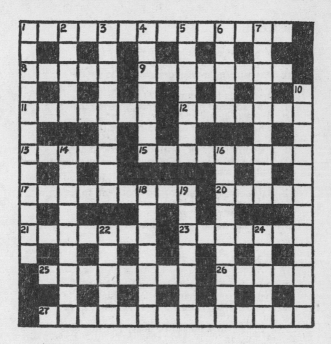

Solution to 30

ACROSS

1 Prophet; 5 Palmist; 9 Sibyl; 10 Wood-notes; 11 Attraction; 12 Leda; 14 Clairvoyant; 18 Nostrodamus; 21 Hold; 22 Soothsayer; 25 Swiveller; 26 Ox-bow; 27 Extorts; 28 Warbler.

DOWN

1 Postal; 2 Orbits; 3 Half A Score; 4 To Wit; 5 Phonogram; 6 Land; 7 In The Way; 8 Test Acts; 13 Horse-shoer; 15 Androcles; 16 Unchaste; 17 Psalmist; 19 Symbol; 20 Drawer; 23 Throw; 24 Seer.

32

ACROSS

1. Perhaps mechanics land by river (6-5).
8. Comedian is backed in the 1.50 (4).
10. Downstream in Glamorganshire, below the surface (10).
11. Draught in the room, say? (4).
14. In a backward part of France, love the dialect (5).
15. Toy of little value? (6).
17. Behaviour gets airman into trouble (6).
19. 10 sober members come in quietly (5, 4, 6).
20. Friend has difficulty with canvas backing (6).
22. Make known view about meat (6).
23. Children see the outcome? (5).
24. Complaints—one's about students (4).
27. Hat-maker takes girl round continent, to see building of a saint (10).
28. Dull poet? (4).
29. Tribe has doom concealed from it (11).

DOWN

2. Defeat for our new transport head? (4).
3. Types of sour durian used in Pakistan (4).
4. Small sleeping place—that is the word, of course (6).
5. Philistine abbé translated quarter of this book (3, 5, 2, 5).
6. Gross foreign friend upsets prophet's daughter (6).
7. Post Office man had three pounds in change after quarrel (7, 4).
9. Roots out forgery in the cited areas (10).
12. Robust types on range in Worcestershire (11).
13. Refuse to take girl as scullery-maid (10).
16. Forsaken a girl (5).
18. Scientist is a scoundrel, that is the conclusion (5).
21. Takes the lead in Henry V? (6).
22. Upsetting eastern drink in feast (6).
25. Certain provisions of parliament? (4).
26. Girl swallows duck immediately! (4).

32

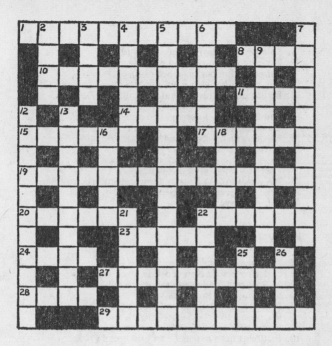

Solution to 31

ACROSS

1 The Prodigal Son; 8 Onion; 9 Shingles; 11 Outside; 12 Declaim; 13 Gorki; 15 Northwich; 17 Fortnight; 20 Liszt; 21 Reliant; 23 Besiege; 25 Penitent; 16 Agist; 27 Understandable.

DOWN

1 Thoroughfare; 2 Edict; 3 Rendition; 4 Discern; 5 Grinder; 6 Logic; 7 Operatics; 10 Amphitheatre; 14 Rural Dean; 16 Hall Stand; 18 Gathers; 19 Tabitha; 22 Amice; 24 Eliab.

33

ACROSS

1. Soldier gives dear Digger a run (9, 5).
8. Nothing so empty as an egg! (5).
9. Sound spring performance (3-5).
11. The prevailing idea is to give the opener money (7).
12. Before noon I race round the country (7).
13. One wrecked vessel smells (5).
15. Bad Samaritan loses right to gain north: he's from the south (9).
17. Obvious disagreement with suitor (9).
20. Clean rough land (5).
21. Novices lose plate—they make money (7).
23. There's always gold in sickness (7).
25. It's small talk in France about spasm (8).
26. Ghastly cover over ancient city (5).
27. Typical traveller (14).

DOWN

1. Instrument picks long eel, jellied (12).
2. Order reversed: New York is black (5).
3. In Scotland, bad roads ran south (9).
4. Sue is not out to negotiate (7).
5. In short, 27 swallows and recurs (7).
6. We object to 'The Times'—that's the custom (5).
7. Oriental in terrific muddle sets things right! (9).
10. Fictional hero makes Gran buy bread (7, 5).
14. Where steps are taken on way to look at box (9).
16. Continent without a shilling has Commonwealth status (9).
18. Creatures in burrows—about a hundred (7).
19. Rebellion of the team? (7).
22. Come in and join (5).
24. Acid revelations of rising composer (5).

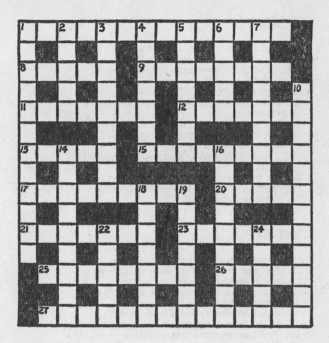

Solution to 32

Solution to 32

ACROSS

1 Ground-staff; 8 Leno; 10 Underneath; 11 Haul; 14 Idiom;
15 Trifle; 17 Action; 19 Under Ones Breath; 20 Burlap;
22 Reveal; 23 Issue; 24 Ills; 27 Athanasian; 28 Gray; 29
Clandestine.

DOWN

2 Rout; 3 Urdu; 4 Domie; 5 The Bible In Spain; 6 Fatima;
7 Rowland Hill; 9 Eradicates; 12 Stourbridge; 13 Cinderella;
16 Lorna; 18 Curie; 21 Pistol; 22 Regale; 25 Diet; 26 Anon.

34

ACROSS

7. The number consumed so to speak (5).
8. Dog laid out T.A. man, possibly (9).
9. Appears to be what the publisher would want to do? (5).
10. Idea arising out of hydrocephalus? (5-4).
12. Guard on the vehicle—so's Ralph—bad arrangement (6-5).
16. Is it ground that could be seen on foot? (4).
17. Books by Henry James, for example (5).
18. Tower executioner? (4).
19. Scientists' rest room's an unusual design (11).
22. Clear love declaration (9).
24. Set forth for the country? (5).
25. Uncivilised person bolts with Scot (9).
26. Stop supplying port? (5).

DOWN

1. Provision for organ transplanting in the city? (9).
2. Malinger to get drink, so to speak (9).
3. Just a broken tree (4).
4. Erin postmen contrive to be everywhere simultaneously (11).
5. Puts away two two-shilling pieces (5).
6. I enter part of the church, being ingenuous (5).
11. Will keep as new in the capital, perhaps (11).
13. He has endless renown, anyway (5).
14. In favour of a proposal for advancement (9).
15. Poe novel—part consists of theatre work (9).
20. Weight of vegetable, we hear (5).
21. Member has nothing to do with prison perhaps (5).
23. Some extra potent gin? (4).

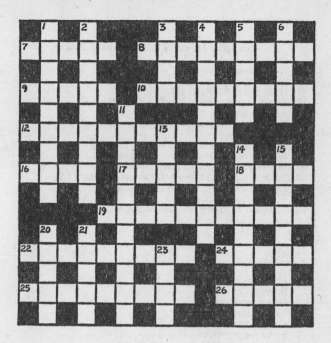

Solution to 33

ACROSS

1 Grenadier Guard; 8 Ovoid; 9 Tap-dance; 11 Keynote;
12 America; 13 Noses; 15 Tasmanian; 17 Plaintiff; 20 Scrub;
21 Earners; 23 Forever; 25 Particle; 26 Lurid; 27 Representative.

DOWN

1 Glockenspiel; 2 Ebony; 3 Ardrossan; 4 Intreat; 5 Repeats;
6 Usage; 7 Rectifier; 10 Barnaby Rudge; 14 Staircase; 16
Australia; 18 Insects; 19 Fifteen; 22 Enter; 24 Verdi.

35

ACROSS

1, 9, 10. Poet refers to nightfall. (Duly thank clew!)
   (anag.) (3, 6, 5, 3, 5, 2, 7, 3).
 8. Fish cuts a suit (5).
 9. See 1 across.
11. Hail! Paddy! (Mean) (7).
12. To some extent he judges her if felonious (7).
13. Arden's one rebuff to the church (5).
15. Toe Charon dislocated may be observed in
    eclipse (3, 6).
17. Shame! Led astray about remote bird (9).
20. Assume as true that one is in position (5).
21. Boy is going round to doctor before one, still (7).
23. Some primitive art he names as made of clay (7).
25. Dispatched in overturned dirt through grating (8).
26. Work Edward chose (5).
27. British politician joins American soldier at first
    light (6, 3, 5).

DOWN

 1. Dare aunt get involved and show fear? Don't
    listen (4, 1, 4, 3).
 2. Girl from Sheffield (5).
 3. Dance thus without hurt (9).
 4. Gadget to suit chaps to a T (7).
 5. Some we perverted without one, alas (3, 2, 2).
 6. Animal weight (5).
 7. Sweet group lie about number being top of the
    pops (9).
10. See 1 across.
14. It's gone to outdo a punter (3, 6).
16. Deliberately made supper? O! No! (2, 7).
18. Veteran, one over a hundred—and ten-to-one he
    could be finished (7).
19. Turn out on completing the team (7).
22. A person at home about to pray (5).
24. Change of heart for one with an aversion (5).

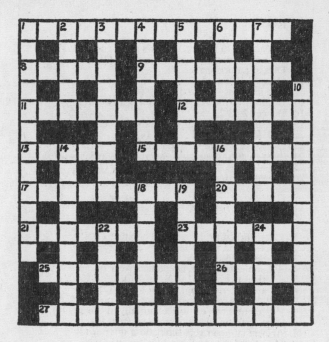

Solution to 34

ACROSS

7 Eight; 8 Dalmation; 9 Seems; 10 Brain-wave; 12 Splash-board; 16 Corn; 17 Kings; 18 Rope; 19 Astronomers; 22 Manifesto; 24 State; 25 Barbarian; 26 Colon.

DOWN

1 Liverpool; 2 Champagne; 3 Fair; 4 Omnipresent; 5 Stows; 6 Naive; 11 Shakespeare; 13 Owner; 14 Promotion; 15 Operation; 20 Carat; 21 Limbo; 23 Trap.

36

ACROSS

7. A marriage in a hovel? That's quite enough! (7).
8. It's very unpopular about the cargo (7).
10. Dickensian assonance (6).
11. Hence 8 19 etc. (1, 7).
12. One in front—of the mirror? (4).
13. Desirous of the skill—to win a brunette? (5-5).
14. Hence 12 23 22 etc. (2, 9).
19. Sad sound of fruit and vegetable flower (10).
22. Tick for the control column (4).
23. Deceptive way to be ungilded (8).
24. Start to go shopping, we hear: that's awkward! (6).
25. For a girl he . . . put down his cloak (7).
26. A heater turning red in parts (7).

DOWN

1. Plates turned up by oriental creature (7).
2. A lot of pain in the face between corners (8).
3. Emphatically it is left out (6).
4. Assembler taking to inside neckwear (8).
5. . . . then I then O . . . Divine! (6).
6. An awful derider, but not of the 22 (7).
9. Ordinary cake made of apples with no gin (5, 6).
15. Representations of objects initially in the city (8).
16. Stays the day among sounds of Paris (8).
17. Ancient surgeon gets time and a quarter (7).
18. Henry and me, or I'm a Dutchman! (7).
20. A copper wants people of quick intelligence (6).
21. My turn to go back is within a discipline (6).

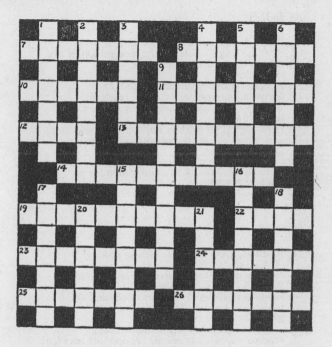

Solution to 35

ACROSS

1 The Curfew Tolls; 8 Ruffs; 9 The Knell; 11 Average; 12 Sheriff; 13 Enoch; 15 The Corona; 17 Fieldfare; 20 Posit; 21 Alembic; 23 Earthen; 25 Strident; 26 Opted; 27 Bright and Early.

DOWN

1 Turn A Deaf Ear; 2 Effie; 3 Unscathed; 4 Fitment; 5 Woe Is Me; 6 Ounce; 7 Lollipops; 10 Of Parting Day; 14 One Better; 16 On Purpose; 18 Ancient; 19 Everton; 22 Being; 24 Hater.

37

ACROSS

1. Where to sign if not so bright (6, 2, 3, 4).
8. Start learning English shortly, then get longer (8).
9. Asserts lost article brought back—that's emphatic! (6).
10. Recipes for hybrid article included (8).
11. Conveyance of property to the French (6).
13. Military leader with lodging place at one Ohio town (10).
16. Organisation for workers upset at ruin done (5, 5).
19. Cure for priest, ten to one with right opening ... (6).
20. ... for headless patient, do arrange a cure? (8).
21. Nothing ruled out, with amplification (6).
22. Sea lane? (4, 4).
23. Browning version in current use? (8, 7).

DOWN

1. Run away from constable? It's so sudden! (4, 4, 3, 4).
2. Holding place for ball, about to run up (6).
3. Production put out by reversal (6).
4. Works are held up by matters of choice (10).
5. In time the Lord sent rain, so Noah goes aboard (8).
6. War drove assembly to run into debt (8).
7. Menace nude girls constitute for opposite sex (9, 6).
12. Totter, but should be able to balance (10).
14. I put compost first in fertilizer—it's good for the hands (8).
15. Animal turns to swallow men in unit (8).
17. A cabin prepared for Baptista's daughter (6).
18. 15, perhaps or Toc H organisation (6).

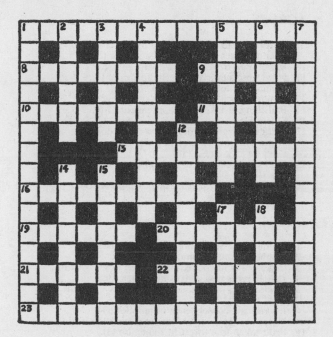

ACROSS

7 Satiety; 8 Loathed; 10 Jingle; 11 L'Allegro; 12 Vain; 13 Faint-heart; 14 Il Penseroso; 19 Melancholy; 22 Joys; 23 Deluding; 24 Gauche; 25 Raleigh; 26 Asunder.

DOWN

1 Laminea; 2 Diagonal; 3 Itself; 4 Collator; 5 Athene; 6 Deirdre; 9 Plain Sponge; 15 Etchings; 16 Sojourns; 17 Veteran; 18 Mynheer; 20 Acumen; 21 Yogism.

38

ACROSS

7. Threatened to have expert in to do repair (7).
8. Painter retires—competitor is coming (7).
10. Many tried hard to believe (6).
11. Stunt upsets everyone in Staffordshire (8).
12. Suitable to hold a command? (4).
13. Would we see a highbrow in this poet? (10).
14. Bad thing, drink, for this attendant (5-6).
19. Shows Helen how to cook, in general (2, 3, 5).
22. Point to animal, as the driver might do (4).
23. Against certain lines of talk (8).
24. Does he kick better? (6).
25. First-class rent collector—and Essex opener, of course! (7).
26. Craft of unusual merit—carries engineer (7).

DOWN

1. Guide includes far more intricate music (7).
2. Robbers prohibit song, it's said (8).
3. Vegetable is ill-cooked—about ten upset by it (6).
4. R.A.F. rents new conveyance (8).
5. In Henry V, has a good deal to drink—upright type, though! (6).
6. It's rise is a consequence of inflation (7).
9. Notes unusually quiet Romeo getting the bird (5-6).
15. Fruit taken to a forest in Flintshire (8).
16. Girl is holding Ron up in Denmark (8).
17. Merchant collects one at noon (7).
18. Shows up cover girl in a perplexing situation (7).
20. Stopped for Nelson? (4, 2).
21. Member enters country in great state (6).

Solution to 37

ACROSS

1 Bottom Of The Form; 8 Lengthen; 9 Stress; 10 Formulae;
11 Landau; 13 Cincinnati; 16 Trade Union; 19 Elixir; 20
Antidote; 21 Louder; 22 Main Road; 23 Electric Toaster.

DOWN

1 Bolt From The Blue; 2 Tenure; 3 Output; 4 Operations;
5 Entrains; 6 Overdraw; 7 Masculine Gender; 12 Accountant;
14 Manicure; 15 Regiment; 17 Bianca; 18 Cohort.

39

ACROSS

1. Carmen had escape—from dessert! (7, 3, 5).
8. Everyone involved copes badly with a heraldic term (8).
9. Criminals used by pastoral people? (6).
10. In writing leader, one means to lead astray (8).
11. Orderly Officer puts sergeant-major in charge (6).
13. Invalid out of terrible famine, and complete designation (4, 2, 4).
16. A thousand thanks in France—in the coal business? (10).
19. Endlessly collecting dried fruit (6).
20. Table to arrange in America (8).
21. Surgeon—ear donor? (6).
22. Enthusiast has open view at the window (8).
23. He carries troublesome Herbert from terraces (9-6).

DOWN

1. Spiritual exercises are boring (9, 6).
2. Account for tax addition (6).
3. Keep back jam (4, 2).
4. Doc Andrews can give a rhythmical performance (5-5).
5. Drawings—empty boxes? (8).
6. Monstrous moron mixed up in rejected petition (8).
7. Business man who is not tone-deaf? (7, 8).
12. A rich Dane's getting a seat (5-5).
14. Irma comes up before the ruler, in India (8).
15. Representative page torn out (8).
17. Tell me a story? It's corn! (6).
18. The lady's hidden gun goes off, causing famine (6).

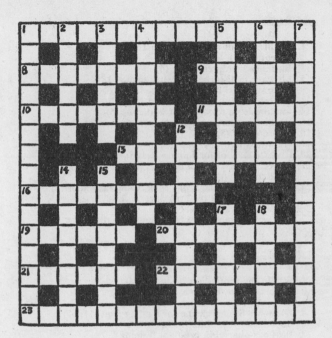

Solution to 38

ACROSS

7 Menaced; 8 Arrival; 10 Credit; 11 Tunstall; 12 Fiat; 13 Longfellow; 14 Night-porter; 19 On The Whole; 22 Skid; 23 Converse; 24 Punter; 25 Aintree; 26 Trireme.

DOWN

1 Refrain; 2 Banditti; 3 Lentil; 4 Transfer; 5 Pistol; 6 Balloon; 9 Stone-plover; 15 Hawarden; 16 Elsinore; 17 Antonio; 18 Dilemma; 20 Hove To; 21 Empire.

40

ACROSS

1. Flight without a penny—a mischievous adventure (8).
5. Blockhead endures blows (6).
9. Mr Page is disturbed by witty sayings (8).
10. Cake supplied by beastly place in the City? (6).
11. Reporter's now at assembly in London (11, 3).
14. Implore Elsie to take part in dances (5).
15. Viceroy appears to seize about a quarter (5).
16. Sword play? (5).
17. He would have it taped! (5).
20. Exclude view of foreign lawyers (5).
22. So Kent mixed school includes part of building in London? (5, 9).
24. Large number take a tiny fillet, being fastidious (6).
25. Last trip on river by Yorkshire town (8).
26. Nursed separate members (6).
27. The way to encourage fish production (8).

DOWN

1. Still in the ventilation business? (4).
2. Trick is smart, but Ena is up to it (7).
3. Standard time, in short, for huge distances (7).
4. Show Mr Stone scheme for loading fruit (11).
6. Supporter of the Bible? (7).
7. Bird has quarrel in pre-fight training? (7).
8. Shropshire town scolds one in Lancashire (10).
12. Important gesture if I have an inclination to make it (11).
13. Lots of guns in Norfolk banks? (10).
18. No one book could give such a feeling of elevation (7).
19. Article on poor rate of building (7).
20. Follow chief highlight (7).
21. Salt sees mate about order (7).
23. Girl gets endless garments (4).

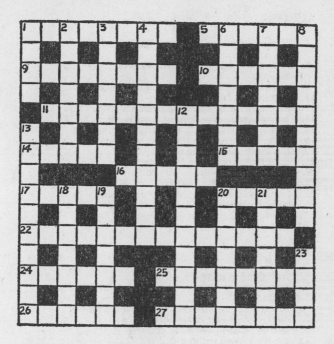

Solution to 39

ACROSS

1 Peaches and Cream; 8 Escallop; 9 Crooks; 10 Misguide;
11 Cosmic; 13 Name In Full; 16 Commercial; 19 Raisin;
20 Schedule; 21 Lister; 22 Fanlight; 23 Stretcher-bearer.

DOWN

1 Pneumatic Drills; 2 Access; 3 Hold Up; 4 Sword-dance;
5 Cartoons; 6 Enormous; 7 Musical Director; 12 Sedan-chair;
14 Amritsar; 15 Resident; 17 Mealie; 18 Hunger.

41

ACROSS

1. Irishman's comments about a footballer?
   (3, 2, 3, 4).
8. Considerable 1 across sometimes given
   standing (7).
9. Couples having lost heart pinch a vegetable (7).
11. Island drink (7).
12. 10 with character lost transplanted a flower (7).
13. City withdrawn from simple country (5).
14. Gives 7 different legs to us: that is nothing! (9).
16. Where, inter alia, you'll find us corrupting art (9).
19. Cast worth re-engaging (5).
21. Lack of motion in rate I adjusted (7).
23. Queen of the Matabele—an ordinary type (7).
24. Get iron from a Papuan (7).
25. Scottish river and English bay? Rubbish! (3-4).
26. Verbal 1 across: the thing's fit and accomplished
    (2, 2, 4, 4).

DOWN

1. 7 includes 7 in mine (7).
2. Unimportant examination engaging a little girl (7).
3. 10 type (9).
4. Some echo pessimists even show feelings for (5).
5. Peel removal to an Essex borough? (7).
6. Material point in soliciting opinion (7).
7. 1 across is usual without end at 1 (12).
10. Meriting 1 across, entreat without two heirs being
    involved (12).
15, 22. Don't touch the spring (5, 4, 5).
17. This broken leg is set by manual dexterity (7).
18. Prophet upset about a right being overturned
    makes fresh examination (7).
19. The retort right away in addition to that (7).
20. Quick progress to valley system of land holding (7).
22. See 15.

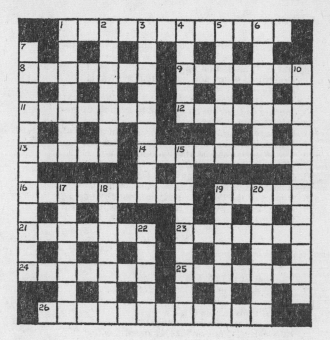

Solution to 40

ACROSS

1 Escapade; 5 Blasts; 9 Epigrams; 10 Eclair; 11 Paternoster Row; 14 Reels; 15 Nawab; 16 Brand; 17 Adept; 20 Debar; 22 Stoke Newington; 24 Dainty; 25 Saltaire; 26 Sunder; 27 Sturgeon.

DOWN

1 Even; 2 Chicane; 3 Parsecs; 4 Demonstrate; 6 Lectern; 7 Sparrow; 8 Shrewsbury; 12 Significant; 13 Broadsides; 18 Emotion; 19 Theatre; 20 Dogstar; 21 Bromide; 23 Jean.

ACROSS

1. A fabrication about lovebirds and love—it's a bit thick, of course! (4, 6, 4).
8. and 9. Illumination on foot (5, 8).
11. Two thirds of ten and half a hundred regularly found (7).
12. Run fast on American petrol—it's a blinder (4-3).
13. Prepare to travel in an attempt to keep them busy (5).
15. One way to turn and greet the scorer at cricket (3-6).
17. Withstanding one Stanley, among others (9).
20. The senior academic takes you in (5).
21. Ginger's suppressed laugh (7).
23. Sign of simple-sounding boy? (7).
25. It's unchristian in one to be a musician (8).
26. Repent of the devil, we hear, in mystic symbols (5).
27. Dance lasting well into the small hours, not ideal for the 15 (4, 6, 4).

DOWN

1. The sign of the George? (7, 5).
2. Not free time in Civil Defence (5).
3. Means of gambling on uncertain prospects for superstitious people (9).
4. Abuse one vehicle for another (4-3).
5. Norwegian islands on lake, frequently with nothing in it (7).
6. Boy? I have a girl! (5).
7. Frankly, the girl put Henry out (9).
10. Very high, spatially or quantitatively (12).
14. Bachelors with money trouble? Beat them with a stick (9).
16. One mineral inside another makes Homer nod quietly (9).
18. Expose a row? (3-4).
19. Playing cricket with engineers on the 'phone? (7).
22. Part of the physical make-up of England (5).
24. A singular fire-iron for a monarchy (5).

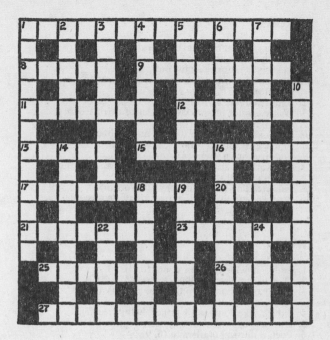

Solution to 41

ACROSS

1 Pat On The Back; 8 Ovation; 9 Parsnip; 11 Madeira; 12 Spiraea; 13 Natal; 14 Eulogises; 16 Australia; 19 Throw; 21 Inertia; 23 Eleanor; 24 Negrito; 25 Eye-wash; 26 It is Well Done.

DOWN

1 Plaudit; 2 Trivial; 3 Nonpareil; 4 Hopes; 5 Barking; 6 Canvass; 7 Commendation; 10 Praiseworthy; 15 Leave Well; 17 Sleight; 18 Retries; 19 Thereto; 20 Rundale; 22 Alone.

43

ACROSS

8. Diggers have a right to be sailors (8).
9. French dream about '51 experience again (6).
10. Medicinal capsule caught out pain (6).
11. Tearing after retreating gunner—and getting there (8).
12. Rent from late arrival (4).
13. Writer creates provincial females of merit (10).
15. Sand put into shovel (7).
16. Quick answer to uncontrolled anger about mail (7).
18. Trams give way to other vehicles (10).
19. The river has a point (4).
20. Old word for superior, first-class sergeant-major (8).
22. I tramp round the hollow (6).
23. False reading (not writing) of flowers (6).
24. It's revealing to take the measure of an abstainer with beer! (8).

DOWN

1. Lady—a fickle one—in opera (6, 9).
2. Dick had a place in Shakespeare (7, 3, 5).
3. That garden comes from social security benefit! (5, 5).
4. Attack, like Jonathan's father, before tea (7).
5. Our railways carry an engineer, brother (4).
6. Poet, a musical craftsman (6, 9).
7. In river battle, he became ruler (4, 3, 8).
14. A particle, is not radioactive in Kent (10).
17. Two friends with webbed feet (7).
21. Misfortunes will soon be forgotten (4).

Solution to 42

ACROSS

1 Mock Turtle Soup; 8 Light; 9 Infantry; 11 Endemic; 12 Tear-gas; 13 Embus; 15 Run-getter; 17 Resistant; 20 Doyen; 21 Snigger; 23 Symptom; 25 Paganini; 26 Runic; 27 Good Length Ball.

DOWN

1 Maltese Cross; 2 Caged; 3 Totemists; 4 Rail-car; 5 Lofoten; 6 Sonia; 7 Uprightly; 10 Astronomical; 14 Bastinado; 16 Endomorph; 18 Airline; 19 Testing; 22 Gland; 24 Tonga.

ACROSS

1. Hide Bella's bits of clothing (10).
8. Issue a period return (4).
10. Rage, perhaps, as a driver might do? (6, 4).
11. Look average, so to speak (4).
13. In Paris, met an artist and composer (7).
15 and 17. Low offer to have one's consideration? (1, 5, 3, 4, 8).
16. Satisfies eastern backer, in this respect (6).
17. See 15.
18. 24 among the hundreds in this resort (6).
20. Late marshal took bread and swallowed his tongue! (6).
21. Lecturer and biologist has sore misgiving about someone (7).
22. Hard thing to get into this club? (4).
25. Making a synopsis is forbidden in a lot of different places (10).
26. Reputation in the bar? (4).
27. Always pleased to go to quarters in Florida (10).

DOWN

2. Every one in the teaching profession? (4).
3. Chief goal-scorer, perhaps? (4).
4. Great woman for crime! (6).
5. Reading a bulb catalogue? (5, 10).
6. Lee awkwardly embraces own Scots girl (6).
7. Worker gets break in the mess at noon (10).
9. People carry help to chief in Berkshire (10).
12. Corroborating support given to complaint about batting (7, 3).
13. Game fish is given to the Queen (7).
14. Takes for granted having a problem in rough seas (7).
15. Loves getting diseases? (10).
19. Comfort from the heater expert (6).
20. Nag stumbles after swan in the island (6).
23. For a rising port, look round Gateshead (4).
24. Some clean, neat girl? (4).

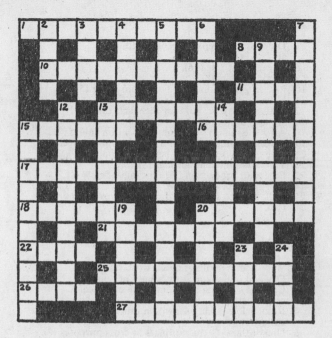

Solution to 43

ACROSS

8 Mariners; 9 Relive; 10 Cachet; 11 Arriving; 12 Tear; 13 Galsworthy; 15 Dustpan; 16 Riposte; 18 Streetcars; 19 Dart; 20 Archaism; 22 Armpit; 23 Floral; 24 Telltale.

DOWN

1 Madame Butterfly; 2 Richard The Third; 3 Death Grant; 4 Assault; 5 Brer; 6 Oliver Goldsmith; 7 Ivan the Terrible; 14 Whitstable; 17 Palmate; 21 Ills.

45

ACROSS

1. Did without sleep as arranged although annoyed (10).
6. Engagement ring? (6).
9. Broods in cars (8).
10. Proved guilty if located away from home (5, 3).
11. Ushant's favourite resorts (6).
12. Artless I may be, but they face facts (8).
14. An approach open to the river (8).
16. After the month's beginning is bent on ruling (8).
19. Arrested development of a Scottish town indeed (8).
21. Humorist has a success, being very modern (4, 2).
22. Time soon modifies feelings (8).
23. Fine malt production from a chain of cells (8).
24. Fell and kept quiet (3, 3).
25. Follow on to where the dressing-rooms often are (10).

DOWN

1. Wilts doctor so upset about work (6).
2. Dry and initially taciturn school of opinion (4).
3. Carnage suffering beheading with evidence of amusement (8).
4. Responsible quality shown, in other words, by the cashier (14).
5. One of those German princes at cross purposes (7).
7. Loved being in the lead or edging away (6).
8. Claw and hit here (anag.) (No! No!) (6, 4, 4).
13. It's safe to dive deep (5).
15. As jaded as the salesman who's lost his orderbook (8).
17. An impression 11 noted possibly (7).
18. Lion traps worker in the shed (4-2).
20. Counted out in the ring twice—passé (3, 3).
22. Spitfire before review (4).

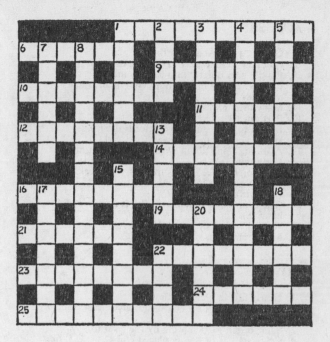

46

ACROSS

4. Girl put poor Abe second (8).
8. Odd pair to take part in Shakespeare (6).
9. Reptile goes quietly into the ground (8).
10. Plunders attendants without complaint being made (8).
11. Many face it with a smile (6).
12. Poet quietly interrupts poet (8).
13. Return to fruit stand in Staffordshire (8).
16. Writer appears to run away from girl (8).
19. Alarming thing about weak management in Derbyshire (8).
21. Take some coffee? Bless me, it's very weak! (6).
23. A large number in the only hut settlement in Devon (8).
24. 'The Chimes,' if taken wrongly, is a source of harm (8).
25. Walked with doctor in wild dale (6).
26. Might remain as chief support (8).

DOWN

1. Nearly fills in a child's time (7).
2. Is unsatisfactory on board, but gives least trouble to officer (9).
3. Some began gesticulating by the river (6).
4. Crazy actions of highly placed clubs? (4, 2, 3, 6).
5. Natives get fair treatment on vessels (8).
6. Genuine Moslem leader for the province (5).
7. Carl is disturbed about strike in Pakistan (7).
14. Also goes to court poor Mab in Queensland (9).
15. Writer gives point to Violet's work (8).
17. Woman takes up a love story by Burney (7).
18. Absorbing work of some writer? (7).
20. A sort of green in the town? (6).
22. Francis is cured (5).

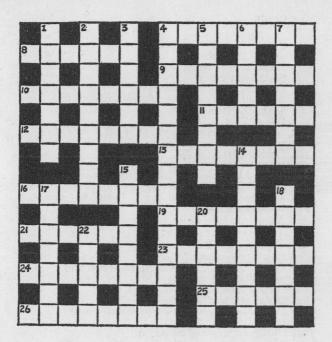

Solution to 45

ACROSS

1 Displeased; 6 Washer; 9 Clutches; 10 Found Out; 11 Haunts; 12 Realists; 14 Overture; 16 Decision; 19 Detained; 21 With It; 22 Emotions; 23 Filament; 24 Lay Low; 25 Understand.

DOWN

1 Droops; 2 Sect; 3 Laughter; 4 Accountability; 5 Elector; 7 Adored; 8 Handle With Care; 13 Sound; 15 Listless; 17 Edition; 18 Lean-to; 20 Too Old; 22 Etna.

47

ACROSS

1. Crowds made fools of by the symbol of the in-security of happiness (5, 2, 8).
8. I claim in error being hostile (8).
9. Frank impressions (6).
10. The ropes artists recognised (8).
11. Waterfall he viewed from a Scottish sea-loch (6).
13. Solemn duet arrangement is free from attack ... (10).
16. ... but trio (reel as transcribed by us) is weak in attack (10).
19. Come down on fire (6).
20. Using a number out of sorts (8).
21. Nymphs from Dante's 'Inferno' read Sophocles (6).
22. Flower for a modest girl (8).
23. Walking up to reality on Mull, I insisted on development (15).

DOWN

1. Losing one's foothold thus expressed in a brief interpolation (8, 2, 1, 4).
2. God, sir, is nothing if overthrown (6).
3. Moves aimlessly by drove-roads (6).
4. Notoriously wideawake about an award—over a pound (10).
5. Unspeakable cad, of course (8).
6. Girl surrounded by metal arranged in layers (8).
7. Delay a decision on 1 across? (7, 8).
12. Composer to drive men to distraction (10).
14. Crafty boxers? (8).
15. Lily's type had Poles all agog (8).
17. Decree of a lumberjack? (6).
18. Brose I prepared as foodstuff (6).

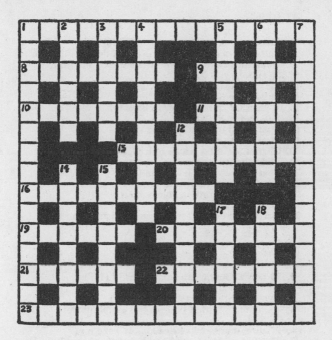

Solution to 46

ACROSS

4 Beatrice; 8 Portia; 9 Terrapin; 10 Pillages; 11 Camera;
12 Thompson; 13 Tunstall; 16 Penelope; 19 Bakewell; 21
Feeble; 23 Lynmouth; 24 Mischief; 25 Ambled; 26 Mainstay.

DOWN

1 Tonight; 2 Stalemate; 3 Ganges; 4 Bats In The Belfry;
5 Africans; 6 Realm; 7 Chitral; 14 Toowoomba; 15 Novelist;
17 Evelina; 18 Blotter; 20 Kendal; 22 Bacon.

48

ACROSS

1. Discrimination means legal action (8).
5. The doctors are intimidating round the Kremlin (6).
9. Housemen have a pull in where they come from (4-4).
10. Marine music for an Irishman (6).
11. Called dog (8, 6).
14. A pleasant spot, as I see in large (5).
15. Fed up instead? (5).
16. First laugh on a record (5).
17. Mount with a musket (5).
20. Chance to find a stroke to leg (3, 2).
22. Light shades for academic sports (9, 5).
24. That's the stuff to give them (6).
25. Academic alternatives to be filled in (3, 5).
26. 'Fie, fie, my Lord! A soldier, and——?' (Macbeth) (6).
27. Hardly the doctor for 22 near Southampton (8).

DOWN

1. 20 down. Gentleman from 8 or 13? (4, 7).
2. Smiled quietly, showing these? (7).
3. German with little time as a god (7).
4, 23. Larceny wasn't odd for this establishment (3, 8, 4).
6. It's tiresome to make one almost wake up (7).
7. There appeared a good number at the show (7).
8. We got moving at length—a spot woolly (4, 6).
12. Animal in a barge called Phosphorus (5-6).
13. November race meeting, one with a 4 (4, 6).
18. One way to bring home bacon—unaccompanied (3-4).
19. Strigil at the door (7).
20. See 1 down.
21. Lute goes round under the world (7).
23. See 4.

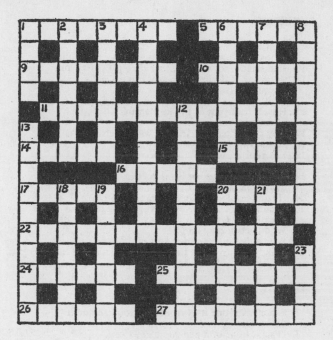

49

ACROSS

1. Stuff to cut in the field (7).
5. Brook confuses Thomas Coxhead (7).
10. Had a tendency to work part time (4).
11. In favour of decimal coinage, it is officially announced (10).
12. Cook gets fresh rise, including a medal (6).
13. How a snake got in the way on the Mississippi, perhaps (4-4).
14. Play gives Lunt dire trouble with direction (9).
16. Spurious pound in safe, possibly (5).
17. Vigorous porter? (5).
19. Player gets the bird (9).
23. Expel doctor and vet involved with I.O.U. forgery (5, 3).
24. Having less feeling for a certain issue? (6).
26. Record order for traveller's beginning to cause uneasiness? (10).
27. Wood gets a bargain (4).
28. Woman's fish is another sort (7).
29. Talk foolishly about the Spanish ecclesiastic (7).

DOWN

2. Sailor takes one into an island group to find a native (7).
3. Distant hope of a penny paper? (5).
4. Cover the said tobacco (7).
6. Trade head gets permit for candle-making (6).
7. Might take two to get spliced? (9).
8. Firm upset drudge and contemporaries (7).
9. Against players getting a share of reward (13).
15. Just about one case appears ambiguous (9).
18. Clumsy brute goes round in a motor (7).
20. Battleship seen by the Lizard? (7).
21. Graceful member in neat outfit (7).
22. General writes tract? (6).
25. Was first to order mount of this pattern (5).

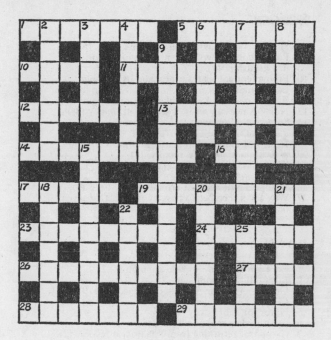

ACROSS

1 Judgment; 5 Moscow; 9 Home-town; 10 Seamus; 11 Clerical Collar; 14 Oasis; 15 Sated; 16 Alpha; 17 Athos; 20 Hit on; 22 Cambridge Blues; 24 Troops; 25 Pro forma; 26 Afeard; 27 Droxford.

DOWN

1 John; 2 Dimples; 3 Mithras; 4 New Scotland; 6 Onerous; 7 Camelot; 8 West Riding; 12 Light-bearer; 13 Nova Scotia; 18 Ham-bone; 19 Scraper; 20 Halifax; 21 Theorbo; 23 Yard.

50

ACROSS

1. He lets 1000 dragons masquerade as pets (6, 8).
9. Poet becomes involved with bishop and oriental in Lancashire (9).
10. Enjoyment comes from bringing us together (5).
11. Basket-maker returned like this? That's right (5).
12. Broken mare and mad rider are united again (9).
13. Noisy American set is upset—most finicky (8).
14. Standard adjustment to his district (6).
17. Take nothing with rank fruit! (6).
19. Lines not damaged in Scotland (8).
22. A weapon supports a promise (9).
24. Weak mediaeval instrument is recorded (5).
25. Subject in Belgium (5).
26. Bird gets rent account around Hawkshead (9).
27. Way for a member to pass by reader. (He saves paper) (5, 9).

DOWN

1. Fool got fab male—made a match (4, 2, 8).
2. Boys tell fibs about sum (7).
3. Getting more varied grain in rugged glen (9).
4. Cleaner keeps quiet about troublesome brat (3-5).
5. Notes for short story? (6).
6. Beast makes row about note (5).
7. Composer returning from Spain is so restless (7).
8. In Iolanthe, master has opportunity to bring up document (4, 10).
15. Permission to give discount (9).
16. Act cut to change name (4, 4).
18. Old franc I enthusiastically held (7).
20. Making left-back sit around, he uses flowery language (7).
21. Language of officer in charge of exercise? (6).
23. First, Eamonn bottled up the hot air (5).

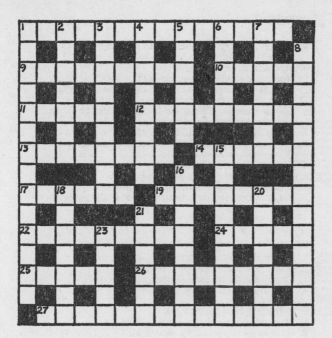

Solution to 49

ACROSS

1 Paddock; 5 Stomach; 10 Date; 11 Proclaimed; 12 Simmer;
13 Show-boat; 14 Interlude; 16 False; 17 Stout; 19 Trumpeter;
23 Drive Out; 24 Number; 26 Discomfort; 27 Deal; 28
Herling; 29 Prelate.

DOWN

2 Arabian; 3 Dream; 4 Caporal; 6 Tallow; 7 Mainbrace;
8 Coevals; 9 Consideration; 15 Equivocal; 18 Turbine;
20 Monitor; 21 Elegant; 22 Common; 25 Model.

51

ACROSS

9. A foreign charge—something to raise the standard (5, 4).
10. Stop within feet, say? (5).
11. No pound notes for medicine? (7).
12. Well, it was the sort the Dormouse mentioned (7).
13. Some hate a Lancastrian to get a duck! (4).
14. Looking out for a situation for the hands? (2, 3, 5).
16. The Warden's confused with Fielding's hero (7).
17. Blockhead takes invalid for an old soldier (4, 3).
19. Child learns nothing new—objective attained! (10).
22. Was coming immediately? (4).
24. Some err badly and show compunction (7).
25. Animals are in the compound (7).
26. See doctor about prince—understand? (5).
27. For example, the way to carry metal in the plant (9).

DOWN

1. Turner fixes a bag to transfer the plant (6, 9).
2. Wood has grave need of treatment (5-3).
3. Carroll's creature gets quarters on old boat (5).
4. They are assumed to be common people without a weapon (8).
5. Bob has a boat to draw (6).
6. Plant deep, standing in rising ground (9).
7. Have to swallow many a port? (6).
8. Might be called figures in a book? (9, 6).
15. Rent falls, causing signs of grief? (4-5).
17. Husks fit for Charlotte's brother (8).
18. Form of transport for moon trip—a bird! (8).
20. Plain little girl upset mine (6).
21. Batsman wanted to get at the beer? (6).
23. Factory is growing? (5).

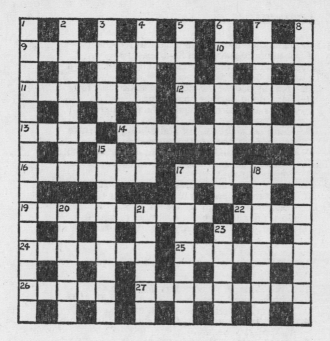

Solution to 50

ACROSS

1 Golden Hamsters; 9 Middleton; 10 Gusto; 11 Osier; 12 Remarried; 13 Fussiest; 14 Parish; 17 Orange; 19 Neilston; 22 Backsword; 24 Wrote; 25 Liege; 26 Thornhill; 27 Stamp Collector.

DOWN

1 Game Of Football; 2 Laddies; 3 Enlarging; 4 Hat-brush; 5 Minims; 6 Tiger; 7 Rossini; 8 Lord Chancellor; 15 Allowance; 16 Deed Poll; 18 Ancient; 20 Tropist; 21 Coptic; 23 Steam.

52

ACROSS

1. Big fiddle—abuses bold treatment required (6, 4).
6. Be about to run one in South-east Asia (6).
9. Student takes antique vessel, half spurious, for a plant (8).
10. Treat fly badly—the means the spider used (8).
11. Fires sound warning on ship (6).
12. Drinks and worries about nothing, ourselves included (8).
14. Editor cut short song of praise—dropped article returned—it's not up to the usual mark! (4, 4).
16. Fleece and plunder to get a seat in the Lords (8).
19. A games cap is my ambition—it holds protection from reality (8).
21. Means of getting pictures arrived before artist (6).
22. Divert cart sideways, put back contents (8).
23. Conceal ailments in decline (8).
24. Gone off with unknown quantities of gas (6).
25. Bolivar, the revolutionary, takes the biscuit! (4, 6).

DOWN

1. Several submarine operators (6).
2. With her mug, Lydia is not exactly beautiful (4).
3. Sold yard material when illegal to do so (5, 3).
4. Entertainment arranged following relief from duty? (6, 3, 5).
5. Surprise—Edward checked development! (7).
7. The Spanish being in the way, put one more into the breech (6).
8. State of the country? (8, 6).
13. Reptile brought back from the Kansas range (5).
15. Hebrew scholar that is in first Grand Llama set-up (8).
17. Love chariot in a musical instrument (7).
18. Mind of tipsy Chelsea artist (6).
20. Actors, or one of twins (6).
22. Drive arranged with one drop of fuel (4).

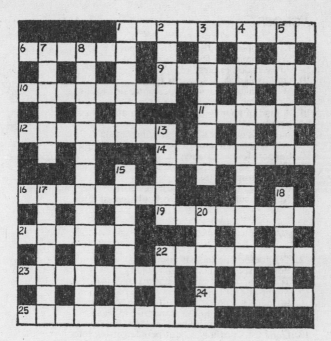

Solution to 51

ACROSS

9 Union Jack; 10 Pause; 11 Nostrum; 12 Treacle; 13 Teal;
14 On The Watch; 16 Andrews; 17 Bill Man; 19 Impersonal;
22 Anon; 24 Remorse; 25 Wolfram; 26 Grasp; 27 Eglantine.

DOWN

1 Burnet Saxifrage; 2 First-aid; 3 Snark; 4 Garments; 5
Sketch; 6 Speedwell; 7 Muscat; 8 Telephone Number; 15 Tear-
drops; 17 Branwell; 18 Monorail; 20 Pampas; 21 Opener;
23 Plant.

53

ACROSS

1. River appears to be right in the road? (6).
5. Wild animals—a few are playful (8).
9. Artist making notes? (8).
10. Isn't as bad as such marks (6).
11. What makes the truth appear prosaic? (6-2-4).
13. Gets home in uniform? (4).
14. A kind of goods—one uncommon about now, possibly (4-4).
17. Badger is an animal with gray parts (8).
18. Transport head appears to demand work (4).
20. Support for the infantry, as it were (12).
23. Girl carries on in Italy (6).
24. State transport? (8).
25. Rats seem to gather in these vessels (8).
26. Appears composed, though badly teased (6).

DOWN

2. Teach everyone to bear pain? (4).
3. For the ship's keel, perhaps? (4, 5).
4. Tell of quarrel at earliest opportunity (6).
5. Might protect the members in the plot (9, 6).
6. Introduces scholars to another extinct animal (8).
7. Employees keep up the standard? (5).
8. Worker gets cut in arm—is upset (10).
12. Quite true, possibly, about people getting into temptation (10).
15. Penny drink of port? (9).
16. Game of the prizefighting era? (8).
19. Might appreciate these flowers? (6).
21. Peculiar charm of a capital to its inhabitants (5).
22. End up carrying quarter of capacity (4).

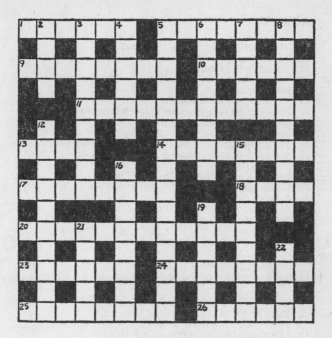

Solution to 52

ACROSS

1 Double Bass; 6 Brunei; 9 Larkspur; 10 Flattery; 11 Shoots;
12 Carouses; 14 Neap Tide; 16 Woolsack; 19 Escapism; 21
Camera; 22 Distract; 23 Hillside; 24 Oxygen; 25 Bath Oliver.

DOWN

1 Divers; 2 Ugly; 3 Lords Day; 4 Boston Tea Party; 5 Stunted;
7 Reload; 8 National Health; 13 Snake; 15 Gamaliel; 17
Ocarina; 18 Psyche; 20 Castor; 22 Derv.

54

ACROSS

9. Absolve, formerly at a single price (9).
10. The bishop fell short of a garden of jewels (5).
11. Naturally it produces respect (7).
12. 'The 21 down we —— in 22 across 22 down' (Macbeth) (7).
13. '. . . 3 to have 23 downed and 8 than —— to have 23 downed' (Tennyson) or '8' (Butler) 'at all' (5).
14. Old Spanish brotherhood provides her with a husband and father (9).
16. The houseman could be 21 down or 23 across (15).
19. A quality of some answers—not bromides, though powdery! (9).
21. Musician who sounds destructive (5).
22. Conclusion of philosophy—that's right—'s science (7).
23. Generous alternative to 21 down (7).
24. Source of architecture one finds in Holy Island (5).
25. Ground I've made by eating (9).

DOWN

1. Proverbially like the unshelled (4, 2, 1, 3).
2. Extra extra? (8).
3. 4. —— than 13, is the 20 (6, 4).
5. Translators' performances (10).
6. Old home of the wise had a lace broken (8).
7. Male journalist dramatically displayed (6).
8. 23 down 21 down was dramatically (4).
14. See a philosopher about erring brides in an East Coast region (10).
15. Yonder gold might produce wood-blindness (10).
17. No 23 down is 8 between those who are (8).
18. Break during school? It follows (8).
20. It goes (without ——?) (6).
21. Party of 23 down, it could be (6).
22. '——s of . . .' (4).
23. '. . . —— be sweeter far Than all other pleasures are' (Dryden) (4).

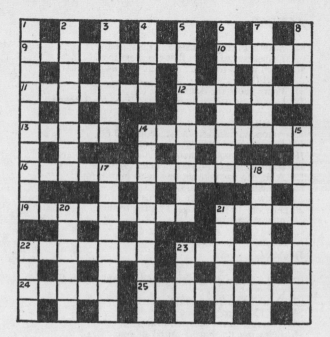

Solution to 53

ACROSS

1 Camber; 5 Gamesome; 9 Whistler; 10 Stains; 11 Matter-of-fact; 13 Flat; 14 Iron-ware; 17 Bullyrag; 18 Task; 20 Perambulator; 23 Verona; 24 Victoria; 25 Steamers; 26 Sedate.

DOWN

2 Ache; 3 Base Metal; 4 Relate; 5 Gardening Gloves; 6 Mastodon; 7 Staff; 8 Manicurist; 12 Allurement; 15 Waterford; 16 Cribbage; 19 Stocks; 21 Aroma; 22 Pint.

ACROSS

1. Malt is France's outstanding feature (6, 7).
9. Disbelieve, partially, that He is existent (7).
10. Claw with which Jack the killer holds the giant's head (7).
11. Poem about the deep in love (5).
12. Denys was originally one entertained by Bacchus (9).
13. 3 with a 3-year-old 4 (5).
15. Actors admitted to the stage in 13 3 (9).
17. Have 41 winks? (9).
18. Spoke for each of them (5).
19. Swineherds get Edward painted (9).
22. A way to live without having to put on fat (5).
23. Time to be resolute (3, 4).
24. Flower girl without a name using force (7).
25. The way to put a finger into the try-line, anagrammatically (13).

DOWN

2. Old wood, a dry object, round the old city in 13 3 (9).
3. Don't express anger! (5).
4. See 15 down.
5. Traveller in the 'lectric railway (9).
6. Being one up. Father raised support (5).
7. Roof coming down: it's no good to hear (13).
8. Give me tins that turn to warnings (13).
10. Shine on the work in 13 3 (7).
14. You conquered Everest last night (9).
15, 4. Literary seat in 13 3 (12).
16. Two movements of the sea in 13 3 (9).
20. Turn pale as a daisy (5).
21. Inversely a border of 13 3 by the sea (5).
22. Study of a 13 3 MP? (5).

Solution to 54

ACROSS

9 Exonerate; 10 Hatto; 11 Sceptre; 12 Delight; 13 Never;
14 Hermandad; 16 Parliamentarian; 19 Dustiness; 21 Luter;
22 Physics; 23 Liberal; 24 Ionia; 25 Devouring.

DOWN

1 Peas In A Pod; 2 Moreover; 3 Better; 4 Late; 5 Renderings;
6 Chaldaea; 7 Staged; 8 Lost; 14 Humberside; 15 Dendrology;
17 Inimical; 18 Intermit; 20 Saying; 21 Labour; 22 Pain;
23 Love.

56

ACROSS

1. Money is for Thompson? (7).
5. Leave players no retreat (7).
9. Author of some far lengthier work? (5).
10. Stacks fruit vehicles (9).
11. Money order? (10).
12. Room with a draught, say? (4).
14. Former aim is altered by people in the trial (11).
18. In favour of males, poor dears, becoming music-lovers (11).
21. Excellent—but not much done? (4).
22 and 25. Novel business centre? (3, 5, 2, 3, 6).
26. Not bound to be in the battle quarter (5).
27. Breaks the silence of the moon? (7).
28. Refusal to take subscriptions—about fifty—in lumps (7).

DOWN

1. He wrote of the country (6).
2. Burning to be a celebrity when about fifty (6).
3. Am I not able to move this bracket? (10).
4. Puts us up to ways of writing mathematical expressions (5).
5. Hermit of note—a rich sort (9).
6. A contract for the orchestra likewise? (4).
7. Shows spirit with a spasm of force and vividness (8).
8. Bird is sent out to get fish (8).
13. Bad dreams about room to be set in order (10).
15. A way to call up an indifferent expression (9).
16. Entertainment upset works (8).
17. Poor boor in the valley might be pressed to call (4-4).
19. Bob takes goblin for a walk (6).
20. Presents proposals? (6).
23. Barbarian carries gold up lake (5).
24. Might race about one (4).

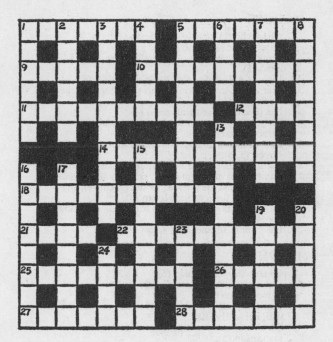

Solution to 55

ACROSS

1 Massif Central; 9 Atheise; 10 Gripper; 11 Epode; 12 Dionysius; 13 Derby; 15 Castleton; 17 Oversleep; 18 Radii; 19 Pigmented; 22 Baste; 23 New Year; 24 Violent; 25 Interferingly.

DOWN

2 Ashbourne; 3 Shire; 4 Field; 5 Tricycler; 6 Appui; 7 Eavesdropping; 8 Presentiments; 10 Glossop; 14 Yestereve; 15 Chester; 16 Tideswell; 20 Gowan; 21 Dover; 22 Brown.

ACROSS

1. Ah! 8 should include meat in the fare (4, 3).
5. Catches the light and makes pan rust (3-4).
9. Imitates the actions of the half returning to Minehead (5).
10. Include a duck for 6's Greek equivalent (9).
11. The wide consideration given to further scholastic work? (5, 5).
12. Northern prelate turns gown (4).
14. Satisfactory account for former play about a troubled wain (7, 4).
18. Ran to a rum at high Turkish station where 20 stayed (5, 6).
21. On equivalent flower in international organisation (4).
22. Lay burden on weigh-chart, possibly (6, 4).
25. Slightly roast me a book, or document (9).
26. Cry a wife for 6 in the Koran (5).
27. Ensures grave surroundings for giving directions to doctors (7).
28. Pithy plant for cleaning vessel (3-4).

DOWN

1. 6's son allowed to play (6).
2. Get me a sort of protoplasmic body for sexual reproduction (6).
3. 6 will be found in old one of these: more than one will, evidently (10).
4. Smith's achievement being put in at the inspection (5).
5. Perfect fruit, we hear, to open the innings (5, 4).
6. Man who made 20 without exclamation? (4).
7. Artist at front of boat: one appeared as a sign to 6 (8).
8. Measure beams for holding short pointed metal objects (3-5).
13. 'The crown, the sceptre, —— will all be mine,'—but we had nasty fall! (3, 3, 4).
15. Describes a house with no provision for stoical discussions (8).
16. Redden, being reduced to mere pulp (8).
17. Such a person may be upset at a court (8).
19. Emotional force responsible for appearing twice in the swimming-pool (6).
20. Container of law-tables, or means of salvation for six (3, 3).
23. Assessed animal above man (5).
24. Keep quiet measure for 6's son (4).

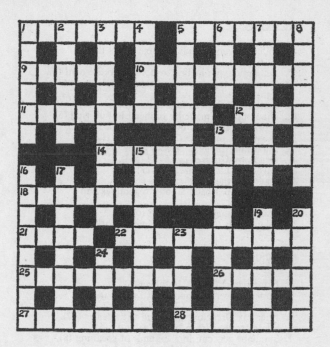

ACROSS

1 Francis; 5 Abandon; 9 Arlen; 10 Rickshaws; 11 Commission; 12 Hall; 14 Examination; 18 Promenaders; 21 Rare; 22 The Heart Of; 25 The Matter; 26 Loose; 27 Selenic; 28 Nodules.

DOWN

1 France; 2 Aflame; 3 Cantilever; 4 Surds; 5 Anchorite; 6 Also; 7 Dramatic; 8 Nestling; 13 Marshalled; 15 Apathetic; 16 Operates; 17 Door-bell; 19 Stroll; 20 Offers; 23 Huron; 24 Main.

58

ACROSS

1. Indian buyers include new cart—it's the custom (8).
5. Lethargic types incline to decay in retirement (6).
9. Conceited and greedy, perhaps? That's about right (8).
10. I enter buildings to find children (6).
12. Nine mistakes made by redhead in bull ring (5).
13. Work out the back bundle, so to speak (9).
14. In general, puts together platitudes (12).
18. Important things in cricket game (5-3-4).
21. Drunk by Gulliver in 1699? (5-4).
23. Girl from Lancashire? Never! (5).
24. Shelter in the boat? (6).
25. I get fruit put back among vegetables and flowers (8).
26. Examinee might be missed? (6).
27. Like female to study Maugham's work? (8).

DOWN

1. None report the rise in fabric (6).
2. Look in a certain quarter in France (6).
3. Flier—difficult to get him right! (5-4).
4. Price Mr Greenlove arranged with dealer (12).
6. Some protagonist in New Zealand? (5).
7. Standard gets cut, in a manner of speaking (8).
8. Red spies get disturbed and scatter (8).
11. Mr Barret's son diverts the actors (4-8).
15. Girl takes on something possibly due to weakness (9).
16. Despise love stories, possibly (8).
17. Honest skill is mounting, in our view (8).
19. Stop in time? (6).
20. Somebody seen by somebody else (6).
22. Look over the practice of a parasite (5).

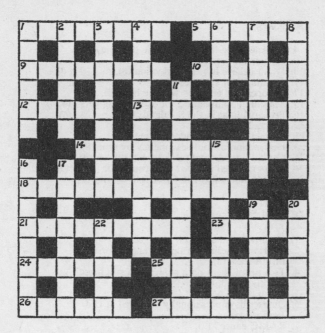

Solution to 57

ACROSS

1 High Tea; 5 Sun-trap; 9 Mimes; 10 Deucalion; 11 Extra Study; 12 Ebor; 14 Explain Away; 18 Mount Ararat; 21 Upon; 22 Charge With; 25 Parchment; 26 Waila; 27 Entombs; 28 Dry-dock.

DOWN

1 Hamlet; 2 Gamete; 3 Testaments; 4 Audit; 5 Sound Pair; 5 Noah; 7 Rainbows; 8 Pin-trays; 13 And The Sway; 15 Porchless; 16 Empurple; 17 Autocrat; 19 Libido; 20 The Ark; 23 Rated; 24 Shem.

59

ACROSS

4, 8. Vale being the shortest one possible (8, 6).
9. Permanent prestige (8).
10. Don't believe in price reduction (8).
11. A canopy for sixpence (6).
12. Co-operative effort to win the lady (8).
13. Searching examination for aspiring coppers? (4, 4).
16. Principal light in the Shetlands (8).
19. Sparta? (3, 5).
21. Counsel sums up modern crime (6).
23. Destruction of footwear merely by time (8).
24. Capital improvement due to enthusiasm (8).
25. Dress material reduced by a penny for the girl (6).
26. Flatter impossibly? It's Death to Shirley (8).

DOWN

1. Fruit-tree and a crop it produces (7).
2. Settle with hesitation on a draught-horse (9).
3. Bird disease (6).
4. Two people bent on a slow death still more
   quickly? (6, 3, 6).
5. Lamb chef d'oeuvre? (5, 3).
6. Quarter-days occasionally observed at Old
   Trafford (5).
7. RAMC dance? (7).
14. The hat he left out's the hat he's forgotten: say
    no more! (5, 4).
15. 21 to cook in Derbyshire (8).
17. Musical direction, one provided by a poet (7).
18. Proceeding by the way with dramatic production
    (7).
20. Confectionery for the panel (6).
22. Their energy constricts the girl (5).

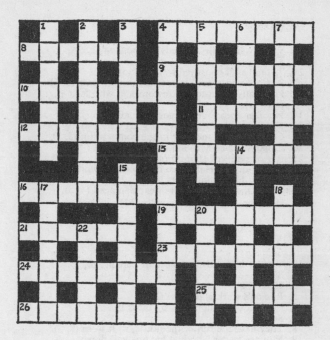

Solution to 58

ACROSS

1 Practice; 5 Torpid; 9 Priggish; 10 Bairns; 12 Inner; 13 Elaborate; 14 Commonplaces; 18 Pitch-and-toss; 21 Small-beer; 23 Irene; 24 Dugout; 25 Petunias; 26 Sitter; 27 Ashenden.

DOWN

1 Poplin; 2 Amiens; 3 Tiger Moth; 4 Costermonger; 6 Otago; 7 Parlance; 8 Disperse; 11 Barn-stormers; 15 Lassitude; 16 Episodes; 17 Straight; 19 Period; 20 Person; 22 Louse.

60

ACROSS

1. War's war, so Bond needs weapons (4, 3, 6).
10. The above (3, 6).
11, 7. Dull stuff conveyed by canal (5-5).
12, 3. Continue to feed thus and study in Beds (5, 5).
13. Physically changed article comes in with false teeth (9).
14. Number about three times as quaverous (7).
16. Fishing boat at the Travellers' Rest? (3, 4).
18. Courage! He'll meet 'er in the competition (5, 2).
20. Edgar Wallace hero hid in the bamboos (7).
21. Act or sing—or split up (4, 5).
23 and 23 down. Half price in black and white? (5, 5).
24 and 22. For making cuts in films? (5-5).
25. Try to find Smith with left ear damaged (4, 5).
26. He takes simplicity for cruelty (13).

DOWN

2. Yonder is an obvious piece of heredity (4, 5).
3. See 12.
4. 12.00 (7).
5. Racine's work is poison! (7).
6. Revolutionary uprisings by birds (9).
7. See 11.
8. They have the run of the house, as it were (8, 5).
9. Military leader who had his ups and downs (3, 4, 2, 4).
15. Military resident giving a hostile reception? (9).
17. Fossils destroyed by Saul (9).
19. Sportive—almost no room in the Theatre (7).
20. Beer's another drink (7).
22. See 24.
23. See 23 across.

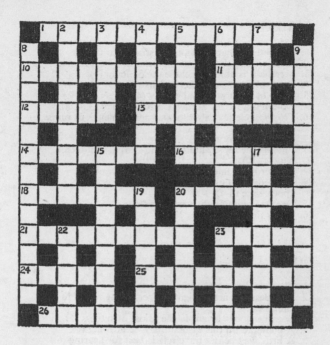

Solution to 59

ACROSS

4 Farewell; 8 Speech; 9 Standing; 10 Discount; 11 Tester;
12 Together; 13 Acid Test; 16 Mainland; 19 Fit State; 21
Advice; 23 Sabotage; 24 Interest; 25 Elaine; 26 Leveller.

DOWN

1 Apricot; 2 Percheron; 3 Thrush; 4 Faster and Faster; 5
Roast Pig; 6 Wides; 7 Lancers; 14 That's That; 15 Bakewell;
17 Andante; 18 Staging; 20 Tablet; 22 Irene.

61

ACROSS

9. Macbeth, perhaps, uncouples stray loco (5, 4).
10. Pertaining to the arm of the beautiful Narcissus (5).
11. Merchant is able to include mixed loam (7).
12. Remembers the engineers' visits (7).
13. A cat of great potential energy (4).
14. No alternative for Sidney Carton in play (3, 4, 3).
16. Trusty circle for experimental performances of plays (3-4).
17. I long to be mean (7).
19. Intelligence representatives who deal in non-secret papers (10).
22. I get cross at finding the vehicle in reverse (4).
24. Cooked pie in metal containers to preserve tidy appearance (3-4).
25. Deeply imbue English artist in this (7).
26. Many times this power? (5).
27. Clio has us worried, privately (1, 4, 4).

DOWN

1. Time-stealer is off-putting (15).
2. Heartless gay artist (right-winger) going round in circles (8).
3. Beginner looks bright in the midst of success (5).
4. A container in this fashion may be growing (8).
5. A little way before the circle is best for hearing (6).
6. Juicy sort Clunes cut out (9).
7. Liquid entrance in strong cry (6).
8. In spare time Bryn is for government by elders (15).
15. Greek character, French actor, bad son, make significant changes (9).
17. A favourable place, where people may be tempted to make daring exposures (2, 3, 3).
18. The return of the island to the animal can be tolerated (8).
20. Distorts the keys for harp-tuning (6).
21. Am seen arranging to bring together (6).
23. A soldier has a short way to take in livestock to feed (5).

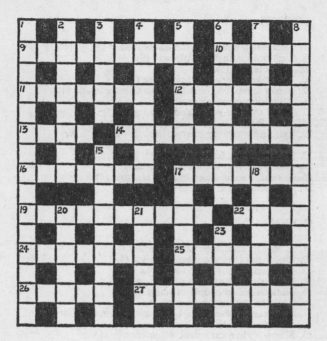

Solution to 60

ACROSS

1 Bows and Arrows; 10 One Across; 11 Ditch; 12 Eaton; 13 Denatured; 14 Trembly; 16 Car Park; 18 Cheer Up; 20 Bosambo; 21 Take Apart; 23 Penny; 24 Flick; 25 Feel After; 26 Heartlessness.

DOWN

2 Over There; 3 Socon; 4 Noonday; 5 Arsenic; 6 Redstarts; 7 Water; 8 Domestic Staff; 9 The Duke Of York; 15 Barracker; 17 Ammonites; 19 Playful; 20 Bitters; 22 Knife; 23 Plain.

62

ACROSS

7. Dickensian enthusiast embraces soldier (5).
8. Light music might be played? (9).
9. King Henry? (5).
10. Tree takes charge in Hampshire (9).
12. A god appears to count on music in the island (11).
16. A division of liquor profit (4).
17. Drink that the gourmand might get? (5).
18. Lots of eggs for Miss Macaulay, say? (4).
19. Left minor to bear charge, though without dowry (11).
22. Sailor appears to counter-attack in battle? (9).
24. Guide one into the ground, perhaps (5).
25. In time, various pairs become unequal (9).
26. Highland estates include mountains (5).

DOWN

1. Is able to do without a river craft (9).
2. Under the tree, notes broken rock (9).
3. Batsmen coming after Tom? (4).
4. The way a fellow talks of a curse? (11).
5. Hothead killed people of standing (5).
6. Point to work of rising poet (5).
11. It's a sort of slang to a Lancashire town, and one in Somerset (11).
13. Shows up in a cathedral, often enough (5).
14. Splendid lines on wicked anti-reformer (9).
15. Write to knight about single dependent (9).
20. Furnishing a hymn, perhaps? (5).
21. Strikes the ship about the middle (5).
23. Call the builder's demand sound? (4).

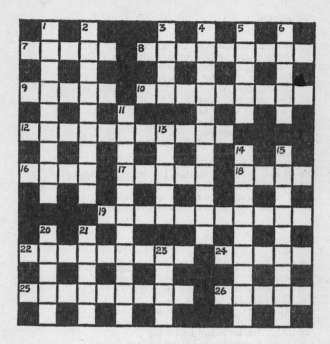

Solution to 61

ACROSS

9 Royal Scot; 10 Ulnar; 11 Coalman; 12 Recalls; 13 Atom;
14 The Only Way; 16 Try-outs; 17 Ignoble; 19 Newsagents;
22 Taxi; 24 Tie-pins; 25 Engrain; 26 Often; 27 A huis clos.

DOWN

1 Procrastination; 2 Gyratory; 3 Flame; 4 Acanthus; 5 Stereo;
6 Succulent; 7 Inflow; 8 Presbyterianism; 15 Mutations;
17 In The Sun; 18 Bearable; 20 Wrests; 21 Enseam; 23 Agist.

63

ACROSS

9. Wish expressed in an undertone close by (9).
10. Perfume has nothing to do with the city (5).
11. Some quite miserable detail (7).
12. Doctor surrounded by animals speaks
    indistinctly (7).
13. Entrance spectators (4).
14. Goat only found in the Lake District (10).
16. Exalt by acceptable eulogy (7).
17. Study green neophyte (7).
19. Authority on hoarding, one who sends out the
    accounts? (4-6).
22. One inch from Bisley (4).
24. Hunt's objective, mother, the others following (7).
25. Rent trouble leads to a storm (7).
26. I had returned the ring in USA (5).
27. Love a girl, one not otherwise engaged (9).

DOWN

1. Suitably humiliated on a modest diet? (6, 6-3).
2. River the French sailor used as a guide (4, 4).
3. Potentate at home once more (5).
4. Safe outside in a good job (8).
5. Allow an order to the hairdresser (6).
6. Glutton from the Roman court (non-U) (9).
7. Dog from an island I note (6).
8. Argued vehemently having put pen to paper?
   (7, 3, 5).
15. Natural, uncomplicated and not abnormal (9).
17. Reaction to birth (8).
18. Carried away from a London district by electricity
    (8).
20. Drift, river fashion (6).
21. Governor of Sparta (6).
23. Doctor converted me about a remote hope (5).

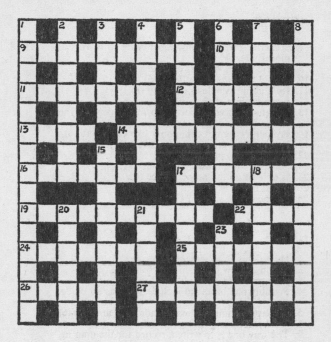

Solution to 62

ACROSS

7 Fagin; 8 Bagatelle; 9 James; 10 Aldershot; 12 Pantellaria;
16 Gain; 17 Stout; 18 Roes; 19 Portionless; 22 Shellback;
24 Pilot; 25 Disparate; 26 Andes.

DOWN

1 Catamaran; 2 Limestone; 3 Tail; 4 Malediction; 5 Wlesh;
6 Eliot; 11 Glastonbury; 13 Aloft; 14 Brilliant; 15 Pensioner;
20 Chair; 21 Slaps; 23 Cite.

64

ACROSS

7. Something funny about a girl being so so very moral! (7).
8. Article put in vehicles or vehicle (7).
10. Bound to get on in college! (6).
11. Rule about people in dwelling (8).
12. Accent might stick to one? (4).
13. Storehouse needs a porter, so I arrange with youth leader (10).
14. Protectors are not commonly like George (6, 5).
19. Young PoW growing up in cave? (10).
22. In place of depravity? (4).
23. Sedative for a musician, perhaps? (8).
24. Is able to go to another dance (6).
25. Artist might draw boat (7).
26. Blasphemous soldier? (7).

DOWN

1. Hide debts from violent collector (7).
2. Climber knew old-fashioned song (8).
3. Silas gets title when about 23 (6).
4. Possibly one means to include silver as an oxide (8).
5. Perhaps cat joins animal standing by another (6).
6. Wife embraces girl of good behaviour (7).
9. The way one is to write a record for the man in court (11).
15. Short man tries to break record (8).
16. Welsh resort's to take on an artist (8).
17. Seat for the emperor's vassal? (7).
18. Awkward predicaments are no handicap to animals (7).
20. Running to get work loading fish (6).
21. Poorly once—getting about again (6).

Solution to 63

ACROSS

9 Alongside; 10 Adour; 11 Itemise; 12 Mumbles; 13 Gate;
14 Buttermere; 16 Upraise; 17 Convert; 19 Bill-poster; 22 Isle;
24 Everest; 25 Tornado; 26 Idaho; 27 Adoration.

DOWN

1 Eating Humble Pie; 2 Pole Star; 3 Again; 4 Sinecure; 5 Permit;
6 Cormorant; 7 Collie; 8 Pressed The Point; 15 Simpleton;
17 Creation; 18 Ecstatic; 20 Leeway; 21 Satrap; 22 Dream.

65

ACROSS

1. Who waited ignoring a disorganised strike? It was and it wasn't worth much (3, 6, 4).
8. To all whom it may concern, every soul's transmigration (10).
9. The date on hand? (4).
11. Take excessive steps to get abroad before the month ends (8).
12 and 1. down. Poet joins Saul and me, historian and king on the hill-range (6, 6, 9).
14. Young soldier suiting a rebel to a T (5).
15. Support 4 for the single (5).
16. Coach having a meal (5).
17. The French fellow is given encouragement (3, 2).
20. Pass quarters in Lancashire (5).
22. Let price be inclusive of children—tall or short (6).
23. '—— and evening bell' (Tennyson) (8).
25. Platform in cloistered aisles (4).
26. 13. Natural observation by 19 surely before 12 1 down wrote it (5, 5, 10).
27. Rum is one of them, made of dinner herbs, that is (5, 8).

DOWN

1. See 12.
2. Deer put to flight burst out (7).
3. Second on the spot (7).
4. Where shooting occurs—not in a cool exchange either (2, 8).
5. She married 19's son (4).
6. Time certain to secure effacement (7).
7. Modified charges in uncomplicated expressions (10, 5).
10. Star ruins (4).
13. See 26.
18. Pantomime character in England and in Ireland (7).
19. Number one, Habakkuk's first man in the Old Testament (4).
20. Low card misdealt leads to hostilities (4, 3).
21. Settled on fire (7).
24. Just entertainment (4).

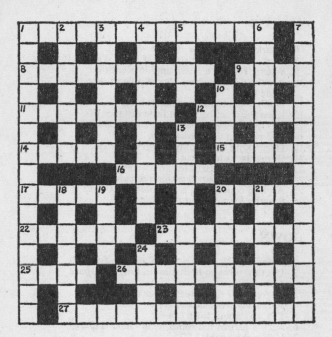

Solution to 64

ACROSS

7 Puritan; 8 Caravan; 10 Girton; 11 Tenement; 12 Burr;
13 Repository; 14 Patron Saint; 19 Stalagmite; 22 Vice;
23 Composer; 24 Cancan; 25 Painter; 26 Trooper.

DOWN

1 Furious; 2 Wistaria; 3 Marner; 4 Magnesia; 5 Marmot;
6 Manners; 9 Stipendiary; 15 Register; 16 Nevinson; 17
Ottoman; 18 Scrapes; 20 Loping; 21 Encore.

ACROSS

4. Charles the Simple's about to buy (8).
8. Garment that won't stay up if Ronald's in it (6).
9. Where 'I heard a lassie sing' in Kent (8).
10. Are the Conservatives almost able to take one side? (8).
11. Don't often trust the gunners! (6).
12. Keep the chief back at a little distance (8).
13. Trouble for horses left among the geese (8).
16. The path up the garden? (8).
19. Dwarf king confused by Glub with 9 (8).
21. Ill-met by sister in cut (6).
23. Tea-time's not right for an assessment (8).
24. Aquarius has a spell within the pale (8).
25. An iced concoction, as opposed to 10 (6).
26. Practise for the Sappers' funeral? (8).

DOWN

1. Islands for sheepish noises about pig-food (7).
2. Unction turns to hesitation in time and space, perhaps (9).
3. I agree with the Latin teacher (6).
4. Judicial obiter dictum? (7, 8).
5. 19's way about town? (4-4).
6. Such a garden hid someone in Genesis (5).
7. Colonial bromide? (7).
14. Perhaps a mad policy needs it specially (9).
15. It's all very fine to raise a lump in a traveller (8).
17. Drink, a thousand years old, for sale (7).
18. No waiting this month (7).
20. Happen to be what doesn't wait (6).
22. European root (5).

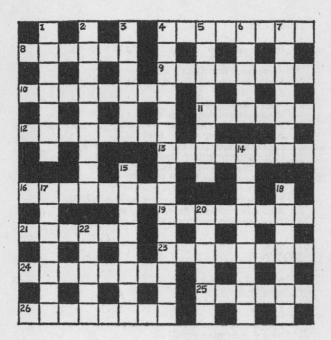

Solution to 65

ACROSS

1 The Widow's Mite; 8 Yourselves; 9 Palm; 11 Outmarch;
12 Samuel; 14 Cadet; 15 Shelf; 16 Diner; 17 Led on; 20 Colne;
22 Rental; 23 Twilight; 25 Dais; 26 Water Water; 27 Inner
Hebrides.

DOWN

1 Taylor Coleridge; 2 Erupted; 3 Instant; 4 On Location;
5 Shem; 6 Erasure; 7 Simplified Terms; 10 Mars; 13 Everywhere; 18 Dandini; 19 Noah; 20 Cold War; 21 Lighted; 24
Fair.

67

ACROSS

1. It's for people to read out—perhaps a young music lover (10).
8. Some poor wretches do artistic work? (4).
10. Manager and Col. Turner compose song and dance (10).
11. Might hold water? (4).
13. Young form-filler, perhaps (7).
15. Incorrect about the whole song (6).
16. About to give up and go back (6).
17. Resort to same new purser for change (6-5-4).
18. Call on me to retire? That's sickening (6).
20. Shoot the tenderfoot? (6).
21. Officer gives pass before 1 50 (7).
22. Some improvident poet (4).
25. Eventually proving to mean expulsion? (7, 3).
26. Also an eye-opener for the retiring girl (4).
27. Tends to go round amid various servants (5-5).

DOWN

2. Rush to get stock? (4).
3. Spot cash? (4).
4. Is approached about entering letters for the dean (6).
5. Play should be taken slowly? (9, 6).
6. Bird gets evening work? (6).
7. Get money on equipment, as a driver might do (6, 4).
9. Devices of sellers, perhaps (5, 5).
12. Citizen is unsettled by lag in wages (10).
13. Sententious airman changed coin (7).
14. Makes us very sad, so much rent, perhaps (7).
15. Took part in play—got knocked down? (6, 4).
19. Daily work of soldiers? (6).
20. O'Casey takes church sitting (6).
23. Many have trouble taking up music (4).
24. Horses found with a pin? (4).

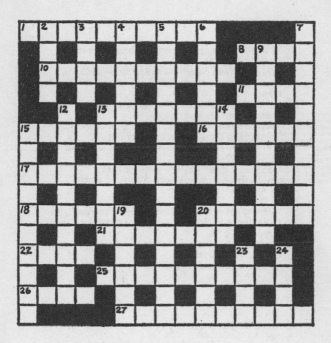

Solution to 66

ACROSS

4 Purchase; 8 Sarong; 9 Sandgate; 10 Cantoris; 11 Rarely;
12 Maintain; 13 Glanders; 16 Primrose; 19 Nibelung; 21
Tmesis; 23 Estimate; 24 Waterman; 25 Decani; 26 Rehearse.

DOWN

1 Bahamas; 2 Continuum; 3 Egeria; 4 Passing Sentence; 5
Ring-road; 6 Hagar; 7 Settler; 14 Diplomacy; 15 Gossamer;
17 Rummage; 18 Instant; 20 Betide; 22 Swede.

68

ACROSS

1. In front of the queen, perhaps because taken in (See 5 down) (6).
5. When the play comes off? (See 5 down) (3, 5).
9. Factor in equestrianism in Beau Brummel's day? (8). .
10 and 3. Boisterousness—the cause of 5 down 5 across 1 (6, 2, 7).
11. Turning inside out, over inn riots possibly (12).
13. Some claim Picts concealed warriors (4).
14. Still incomplete without reference to a former bass (3, 3, 2).
17. USSR in a quiet reunion—national (8).
18 and 22. Project experienced 5 down 5 across 1 (4, 4).
20. 10 (12).
23. Keeps quiet yet may cause 5 down 5 across 1 (6).
24. Indian only having fair deserts according to Dryden? (3, 5).
25. The moving spirit in committee—liable to support Eros, confound it! (8).
26. Watch dispatched by railway (6).

DOWN

2. Some simple, crude linen (4).
3. See 10.
4. Game, one up and thrice confused (6).
5, 5 Across, 1. 'Ref: Grant me boon then if tight here' (anag.) (3, 7, 5, 3, 5, 6).
6. Fundamentals of weather (8).
7. Kings and princes—just in case the final point is not seen (5).
8. Past students (10).
12. Printing licence obtained through a little mischief on the border in the city (10).
15. Opera—Lehar's first with a Rhone setting in G (9).
16. Permits what can be less nice (8).
19. Deep fellows once varied (6).
21. Deck or dock (5).
22. See 18.

ACROSS

1 Promenader; 8 Etch; 10 Carmagnole; 11 Main; 13 Leveret;
15 Ballad; 16 Recede; 17 Weston-super-Mare; 18 Emetic;
20 Sucker; 21 Colonel; 22 Ovid; 25 Turning Out; 26 Edna;
27 Nurse-maids.

DOWN

2 Race; 3 Mark; 4 Neared; 5 Dangerous Corner; 6 Roller;
7 Change Gear; 9 Trade Marks; 12 Glaswegian; 13 Laconic;
14 Tearful; 15 Bowled Over; 19 Column; 20 Seance; 23 Coda;
24 Stud.

ACROSS

1. Turn away broom somehow, sweeping through the city (5, 8).
8. Recent error put sheet out of proportion (10).
9. Hit with retrograde instrument of punishment (4).
11. Having taken into care by arrangement, gets response (8).
12. Exhort companion to argue with no upstart (6).
14. Any number held to harass (5).
15. Matches seldom include game (5).
16. Conspiracy includes one who will get it off the ground (5).
17. Cartoonist was a worker (5).
20. First impression, but it leaves no room for doubt (5).
22. Not Susan, back at the station? (6).
23. Engineer with spade about right for applying manure (8).
25. One of pair to win, nothing less (4).
26. Seized possessions and died over the exertion (10).
27. Prepare land, hire stuff for a home (9, 4).

DOWN

1. Capital . . . (5, 4, 6).
2. . . . proceeds for the licensee? . . . (7).
3. . . . proceeding past which one risks proceedings (2, 5).
4. Rain on holiday produces expression of emotion (10).
5. Where one may be drunk or extremely greedy (4).
6. Yet we're out of the wood (3, 4).
7. Direct ways to obtain money (7, 2, 6).
10. Bird with no knowledge of style (4).
13. Poor saps fork out for one of ill-humour (5-5).
18. Dog finds master unyielding (7).
19. God of Bath or Cheltenham (4).
20. Arranged to give piper a penny, settled in advance (7).
21. First, for example, a service book . . . (7).
24. . . . unless Latin is included therein (4).

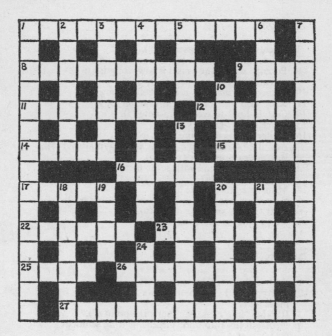

70

ACROSS

1. Cheats southern musicians (8).
5. Fierce animal makes players go back (6).
9. Perhaps where the vessel is low, sounds an alarm? (8).
10. Is prone to make us retreat before long (6).
11. King won't set one free in London (5, 9).
14. Certain lines to women of note (5).
15. River frolic? (5).
16. Writer resists exposure? (5).
17. Admitted having done wrong about Woodhead (5).
20. Bob goes on inferior track (5).
22. Observed structure with some merit in Hertfordshire (14).
24. More imaginary state? (6).
25. Poor Ron gets cold going round in London (8).
26. Shift the dry one over there (6).
27. Don't look so unequalled! (8).

DOWN

1. Part of the problem is sound (4).
2. The principal champion shows the way, in a measure (7).
3. It's right in a preserve, that's the point (7).
4. Put fresh life into poor Greene, getting scolded! (11).
6. Pupil makes the usual mistake about the Merchant Navy, initially (7).
7. Chink in the German boat? (7).
8. Fresh earth is ploughed in the wood (10).
12. Ode woman composed on a single flower (4-7).
13. Bob buys art products in Dorset (10).
18. Perhaps seen with a star of a musical? (3, 4).
19. Little creatures in sleeping-place contract chill (7).
20. 'Kinquering Congs their titles take' (——) (7).
21. Sketch is not in verse perhaps (7).
23. Misfortunes some will say (4).

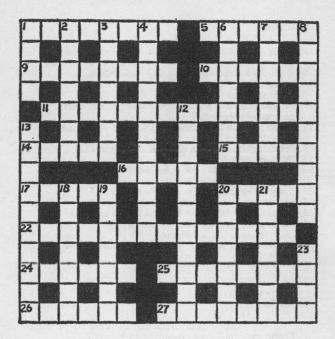

Solution to 69

ACROSS

1 Urban Motorway; 8 Percentage; 9 Swat; 11 Reaction; 12 Charge; 14 Annoy; 15 Chess; 16 Pilot; 17 Emmet; 20 Proof; 22 Euston; 23 Spreader; 25 Twin; 26 Distrained; 27 Furnished Flat.

DOWN

1 Upper Case Letter; 2 Bargain; 3 No Entry; 4 Outpouring; 5 Orgy; 6 Yew Tree; 7 Letters Of Credit; 10 Chic; 13 Crosspatch; 18 Mastiff; 19 Thor; 20 Prepaid; 21 Ordinal; 24 Nisi.

71

ACROSS

8. Good man to slap rouge on or to sit on the fence (8).
9. Disturbs Mister—shortly going back inside, unfortunately (6).
10. Depression can be a blow (4).
11. Make things awkward for 99 coming in late after company representative (10).
12. Small point in Lawrence manuscript is provoking (6).
14. Proximity of northern member to the Cape (8).
15. Prolong sentence (7).
17. About the church—one point gives evidence of acceptance (7).
20. Sport of French-ness is impertinence (8).
22. Fixed purpose under canvas (6).
23. Not so sharp in certain key but boosts ego (10).
24. Sailor-king reversal with a big scoop (4).
25. Sounds again like a bad choice (6).
26. Wildly excited London district has unprogressive support (8).

DOWN

1. Cheap instrument sounds loud and harsh (8).
2. Leave some here (4).
3. Draws out Mussolini in point-to-point (6).
4. French iron-men to start agitation (7).
5. Excuse quietly everything I consumed (8).
6. Being disgruntled, somehow cannot melt (10).
7. It is in a sorry mess through strikes (6).
13. Stopping seedy rep being given an opening and taking charge (10).
16. Belief that may rend church twice, possibly (8).
18. Indian marauder having crooked head and irregular feet? (8).
19. Had big ideas as constant Communist (7).
21. Reduce pressure from world organisation set over the French Church (6).
22. Take in lightheartedly, we hear (6).
24. Ruined toga, the beast! (4).

Solution to 70

ACROSS

1 Sharpers; 5 Bandog; 9 Moorings; 10 Supine; 11 Stoke Newington; 14 Breve; 15 Spree; 16 Hardy; 17 Owned; 20 Spoor; 22 Sawbridgeworth; 24 Utopia; 25 Cornhill; 26 Yonder; 27 Peerless.

DOWN

1 Some; 2 Apostle; 3 Prickle; 4 Regenerated; 6 Alumnus; 7 Drifter; 8 Greenheart; 12 Wood-anemone; 13 Abbotsbury; 18 New Moon; 19 Dormice; 20 Spooner; 21 Outline; 23 Ills.

72

ACROSS

9. The one hope for investors? (4, 5).
10. A new-laid egghead? (5).
11. Inversely the club boar (3-4).
12. A day on the bridge with a 22 (7).
13 and 22. Upper-class fellers want independence (4-4).
14. It's cold in the country; take a fur (10).
16. Bouncer at home in the wood to Fauntleroy? (7).
17. What might a fever do to the glutted (7).
19. Involved in Surrey? That's no problem by itself (10).
22. See 13.
24. Money, perhaps, could end with fuel (7).
25. The ancient story-teller Silas entertains one (7).
26. 3 we hear rung? (5).
27. The spread of the sea? (4, 5).

DOWN

1. Vanity oppresses unless transformed (15).
2. What's wrong with the throat isn't 7 (8).
3. A long hard look at 25 in the South-east (5).
4. The dance makes Rabbit behave like Bear (5-3).
5. Flower people at the station? (6).
6. In the same way 25 may have it in hand (4, 5).
7. What's incomplete in the chest isn't 2 (6).
8. Black Watchdog? (8, 7).
15. Bird on a picnic? (9).
17. One to pick a cloud—with a silver lining? (8).
18. The squalor of the suggested airport (8).
20. Mad girl upset Hamlet next morning (6).
21. Do I sound like an Arab chief? Warm! (6).
23. The primate has his title on the cover (5).

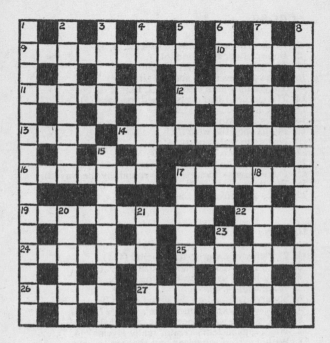

ACROSS

8 Straddle; 9 Alarms; 10 Dint; 11 Complicate; 12 Tempts; 14 Nearness; 15 Stretch; 17 Receipt; 20 Rudeness; 22 Intent; 23 Flattering; 24 Grab; 25 Echoic; 26 Ecstatic.

DOWN

1 Strident; 2 Part; 3 Educes; 4 Ferment; 5 Palliate; 6 Malcontent; 7 Smites; 13 Prevention; 16 Credence; 18 Pindaric; 19 Aspired; 21 Unlace; 22 Ingest; 24 Goat.

73

ACROSS

1. Book written by Diana in ridicule (4, 4).
5. Bobby rather than Bob (6).
9. The opposite to a river of soup (8).
10. A lawyer sees a girl about a girl (6).
11. They simply aren't done (4, 2, 8).
14. The clothes I had overstarched, perhaps (5).
15. Bore like a beaver (5).
16. Rules for swings (5).
17. Fly to open the wine (5).
20. Negotiate with a party? (5).
22. Did a portrait of 23's wife (7, 7).
24. Beast for 5 on the Thames (6).
25. Conventional doctor's whole round, by the way (8).
26. Worthing was in a Southern estuary (6).
27. Bulbs lay broken in the dish (8).

DOWN

1, 2. Plenty of cover in the Marsh? (4, 7).
3. Return of French weapon wasn't alert (7).
4. I'm a hawk, so to speak, in the Cape: volunteer? (4, 7).
6. Supervise abroad by the sound of it (7).
7, 20 down. Taking Touchstone's part? (7, 3, 4).
8. A green tree with a new lease of life? (10).
12. Was Frankenstein's creator really Hyems? (4, 7).
13. With a sort of rag, clean and sharpen the old musical box (10).
18. Make 14 suits up on the Marsh (7).
19. Star worker on Mars (7).
20. See 7.
21. Favourite little woolly jumper? (3-4).
23. Captain of 1 across (4).

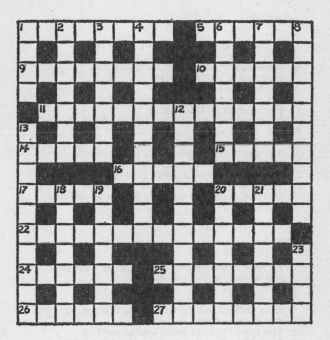

Solution to 72

ACROSS

9 Unit Trust; 10 Adlai; 11 Pig-iron; 12 Monarch; 13 Self;
14 Chinchilla; 16 Lording; 17 Overfed; 19 Simplicity; 22 Rule;
24 Needful; 25 Mariner; 26 Stair; 27 Fish paste.

DOWN

1 Purposelessness; 2 Singular; 3 Stare; 4 Bunny-hug; 5 Stamen
6 Main Sheet; 7 Plural; 8 Highland Terrier; 15 Fieldfare;
17 Optimist; 18 Foulness; 20 Maenad; 21 Calefy; 23 Drape.

ACROSS

1. A hindrance, having a lot of luggage (11).
8. Girl takes a clergyman aback (4).
10. Rustics surround student for a joke (10).
11. Binding is a little lower (4).
14. It's home to a girl (5).
15. Tell of some quarrel at Edgbaston? (6).
17. Firms get on, in this case (6).
19. Seen round the bar, quietly having a break (5, 4, 6).
20. Old lady appears proper to backward girl (6).
22. Also a dandy, some say (2, 4).
23. The way the railwaymen take back cattle (5).
24. Incline towards nurse (4).
27. Bullied by the head strikers, perhaps? (10).
28. Whims of French leader—sad bungling (4).
29. Sots may hate to be mistaken for untravelled types (4-2-5).

DOWN

2. To some degree an afterthought, these plans (4).
3. Still believe Nora's content? (4).
4. I take Anne's scheme to be senseless (6).
5. Author might see new yarn to be unusual (6, 9).
6. River animal turns up: it's on the road, perhaps (6).
7. It makes one drink! (4-3-4).
9. Able types spoke of being worked out (10).
12. Perhaps RAF section lands on the river (6-5).
13. Bungled ode translation—gets beaten (10).
16. City has a second to load metal (5).
18. Horrible creatures, but make some progress (5).
21. Army artillery sections mount up (6).
22. Look at the gamble in it! (6).
25. Emperor loves to hold race (4).
26. Formerly confused with Essex opener (4).

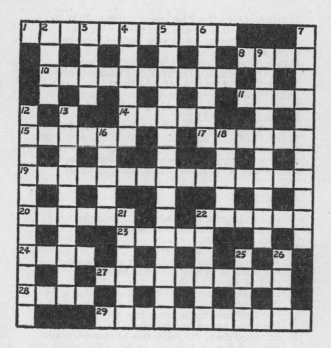

Solution to 73

ACROSS

1 Moby Dick; 5 Copper; 9 Consomme; 10 Penang; 11 Sins of Omission; 14 Rigid; 15 Eager; 16 Sways; 17 Musca; 20 Treat; 22 Painted Jezebel; 24 Oxford; 25 Allopath; 26 Ernest; 27 Syllabub.

DOWN

1 Much; 2 Binding; 3 Drowsed; 4 Come Forward; 6 Oversee; 7 Playing; 8 Regenerate; 12 Mary Shelley; 13 Gramophone; 18 Stiffen; 19 Antares; 20 The Fool; 21 Ewe-lamb; 23 Ahab.

Insertion of the letter P into the solution to 20 in the top diagram yields the first (and perhaps the least known) of a dramatic series; the unclued lights yield the remainder, in order of appearance, as follows, (A) signifying the top and (B) the bottom diagram:

12 (A) 1 down (B); The 17 (B); Her Majesty's Ship 17 (A); The 19 (A)s of 7 (A); 16 (B); 25 (B); 27 (A) 6 (B) (when the house is taken from the state); The 5 (B); 3 (B); 15 (A) of 16 (A); The 13 (B)s; 2 (A) 6 (A)-ed); The 21 (A).

The clues to 1 down (A), 2 (B), 3 (A), 5 (A), 7 (B), 12 (B), 13 (A), 15 (B), 19 (B), 21 (B), 25 (B), and 27 (B) are normal. The remaining lights each consist of two clues run together, the solution to the first belonging to the top, and of the second to the bottom diagram.

ACROSS

1. Spiritual companion, like this German city, devoured the old cinema's life of Garbo troubled with hip (4-4; 8).
5. Pass the rum please! (6); (6).
9. Rodent and urchin outside have river mackerel, disturbing Honorary Doctor in happiness (5, 3; 4, 4).
10. Restitution alters Mars—there's an old ship in his department (6; 3, 3).
12. (5); They have the centre at one end (5).
13. Put a stop to getting a bit oily in the head (9); (9).
14. Supposed change of policy that he makes temporarily at a French African port before this month (12; 3, 2, 7).
18. Rather rosier view of what might increase one's overheads in a French wood even if premeditated (4, 8; 12).
21. (5, 4); Honest sound of cat turning round and round in bed (9).
23. Lady with an aspiration to produce a paper on the electrically charged particle, which makes one weep; (5; 5).
24. The nation wants, in the old way, to make King William the Conqueror's standard come to an end (6; 6).
25. The last camp was wrecked by civets (4-4); (8).
26. Dredge the river before the swan slips—run away in time (6, 6).
27. (8); He estimates fools' gold—about a shilling (8).

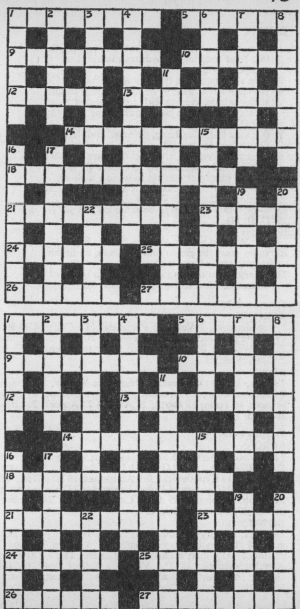

DOWN

1. What's afoot in the Drunken Sailor (6); (2, 4).
2. (6); Neat covering for hydrogen in another compound (2, 4).
3. Ship with a stratum that belongs to me? (4-5); (9).
4. No soup left as awfully small quantities should suffice a little creature with an unfinished house, substandard, whose jaws are the same size (12; 12).
6. (5); (5).
7. (8); One following Lang, perhaps, and the Canterbury leaders (8).
8. Levantine from the wrong set in premature diversion of road and tube, unlikely to change (8: 8).
11. After a smash hit one has to write a melody, alfresco, for snide remarks in a hole in the head, turning to Ian inside (2, 3, 4, 3; 12).
15. (3 6); Train time not to be extended just yet (6, 3).
16. (3 5); (8).
17. (8); (8).
19. (6); Without a blow America fills the gap (6).
20. In an essay the girl to ruin he sits on an organ stop to make love (6; 6).
22. To try to get money from the church is stupid nonsense, when eating like cook (5; 5).

Solution to 74

ACROSS

1 Impedimenta; 8 Vera; 10 Pleasantry; 11 Calf; 14 Nesta; 15 Relate; 17 Cocoon; 19 Under Ones Breath; 20 Duenna; 22 As Well; 23 Runts; 24 Tend; 27 Browbeaten; 28 Fads; 29 Stay-at-homes.

DOWN

2 Maps; 3 Even; 4 Insane; 5 Ernest Hemingway; 6 Tarmac; 7 Half-And-Half; 9 Elaborated; 12 Ground-staff; 13 Bludgeoned; 16 Turin; 18 Ogres; 21 Ararat; 22 Aspect; 25 Otto; 26 Once.

Solution to 75

ACROSS

1 Soulmate; Biograph; 5 Elapse; Mikado; 9 Brown Rat; John Dory; 10 Amends; War God; 12 Trial; Radii; 13 Punctuate; Gondolier; 14 Hypothetical; For An Instant; 18 Hair Restorer; Aforethought; 21 Grand Duke; Incorrupt; 23 Edith; Onion; 24 Anoint; Norman; 25 Palm Cats; Iolanthe; 26 Deepen; Errata; 27 Princess; Assessor.

DOWN

1 Sabots; By Jury; 2 Utopia; Oxhide; 3 Mine Layer; Ruddigore; 4 Teaspoonsful; Paragnathous; 6 Limit; Idaho; 7 Penzance; Anglican; 8 Easterly; Obdurate; 11 In The Open Air; Insinuations; 15 The Yeomen; School Age; 16 The Guard; Patience; 17 Pinafore; Sorcerer; 19 Pirate; Hiatus; 20 Thesis; Endear; 22 Dunce; Roast.